The Whooping Crane

WINNER

1966

The Whooping Crane

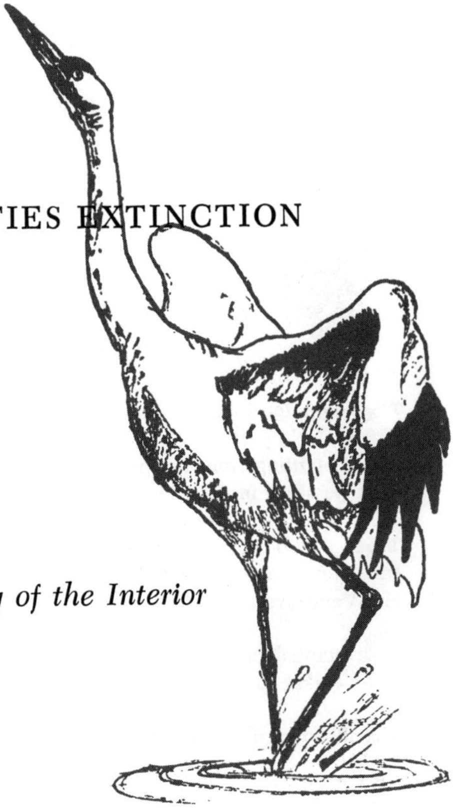

THE BIRD THAT DEFIES EXTINCTION

by Faith McNulty

INTRODUCTION BY
Stewart L. Udall, Secretary of the Interior

New York / E. P. Dutton & Co., Inc. / 1966

FIRST EDITION

 / Library of Congress catalog card number: 66-11544 / Published simultaneously in the United States by E. P. Dutton & Co., Inc., New York, and in Canada by Clarke, Irwin & Company Limited, Toronto and Vancouver.

A substantial portion of the contents of this book appeared originally in *The New Yorker* in somewhat different form.

The illustrations are reproduced through the courtesy of the following:

DRAWINGS / Pages 5, 61, 69, 77, 78 by Robert Allen

MAPS / Pages 44, 117 by R. H. Martin

PHOTOGRAPHS / Page 14, from a watercolor by Louis Agassiz Fuertes; reproduced through the permission of the National Audubon Society and Mary Fuertes Boynton / Pages 17, 73, 75, 79, 87, 109, 162, 185 by Luther Goldman, Pages 42, 60, 132 by W. F. Kubichek, Page 91 by Charles A. Keefer; U.S. Department of the Interior, Fish and Wildlife Service / Page 28 by Allan D. Cruickshank, Page 55 by Dorothy Dingley, Page 154 by S. F. Briggs; National Audubon Society / Page 32; American Museum of Natural History / Page 122 by N. S. Novakowski; Canadian Fish and Wildlife Service / Page 141; New York Zoological Society.

To Richard—with thanks

Acknowledgment

The history of the cranes has been put together from a number of sources. Chief among the published sources are Robert Porter Allen's monograph *The Whooping Crane* (National Audubon Society © 1952), its supplement, *A Report on the Whooping Crane's Northern Breeding Ground* (National Audubon Society © 1956); and *On the Trail of Vanishing Birds* (© 1957 Robert P. Allen, published by the McGraw-Hill Book Company). Permission to quote selected passages has been granted by the publishers. Robert Allen also wrote of the cranes in *Audubon Magazine.* Unpublished records include letters and memorandums from a number of persons in the files of the National Audubon Society and the reports of the managers of the Aransas National Wildlife Refuge.

The author wishes to thank all those who helped her by supplying the information from which this book was formed, and at the same time to make clear that wherever an opinion is expressed it is her own and does not represent the point of view of any individual or organization involved in the whooping cranes' story.

Introduction

This book is the story of a love affair—between a civilized sophisticated Nation and an enormous, elusive bird. We, the people, who slaughtered the bison and exterminated the passenger pigeon, have had a shift of conscience in the last fifty years and have made the preservation of rare species of wildlife one of our national conservation purposes.

The admired conservationist, Aldo Leopold, remarked when the last passenger pigeon died: "For one species to mourn the death of another is a new thing under the sun. We, who have lost our pigeons, mourn the loss. Had the funeral been ours, the pigeons would hardly have mourned us. In this fact, rather than in nylons or atomic bombs, lies evidence of our superiority over the beasts."

Faith McNulty has written of the whooping crane, a majestic, regal, shy bird of the wilderness, almost a relic of the Pleistocene, with great perception and ability. The rescue of this bird from the brink of extinction has become the symbol of our newly developed conservation conscience, and a lesson in the can-do art and science of wildlife management.

This book tells of the steadfast devotion and dedication to a bird; of many persons, particularly Robert P. Allen of the National Audubon Society; of human mistakes, of miscalculations, greed, neglect, skill; of the monumental effort of men and agencies, both private and governmental, to locate the nesting grounds in the Canadian Far North, and to provide a safe sanctuary for the cranes on their wintering grounds which are 2,500 miles apart.

It tells of the tender care of the young cranes by the parents, the ordeal of migration, the ordeal of trying to protect its habitat from man's technological means of advancement. It bugles the vital necessity of gathering scientific data on a wild creature and of carefully analyzing that data for facts and clues to be used in future management and preservation efforts.

As mankind understands more about the creatures who share this planet with him, he is at once ennobled and humbled. His own humanity is enlarged, and for a Nation engaged in conserving almost 100 species of fauna threatened with extinction, the gift is supremely worth the effort.

Stewart L. Udall
Secretary of the Interior

Illustrations

The Whooping Crane

A whooping crane flock in migration. Watercolor by Louis Agassiz Fuertes

1

The whooping crane is a very large and very grand white bird with long black legs, a sinuous neck, and a thrilling, trumpetlike voice. There are, as this is written, approximately fifty of them on earth. Fifty is an extremely small number when it is applied to a species. A year hence, if fortune has favored them, there will be a few more whooping cranes; and perhaps even more the year after that. But if luck turns against them it is conceivable that there will be no whooping cranes at all. The species is that close to extinction.

At one time the whooping crane might have slipped out of existence almost unnoticed. During the years that the cranes have hovered on the brink, a good many other birds and mammals have quietly taken their leave. There are now among us a number of creatures that will not be here a few years hence. It is unlikely that many people will note or mourn their absence. This is not true of the whooping crane. One of several reasons is the stubborn and unexpected tenacity with which the species has held on to life and, in the course of its struggle, enlisted the interest of an ever-widening circle of people. A sort of mystique has grown up around the drama of the whooping cranes' survival, as though, in a manner, it represents the wishes of those people who feel strongly that mankind should not take over the earth at the expense of all other creatures.

The whooping cranes have been called a symbol both of this country's new-found conscience in dealing with wildlife and of its opportunity to atone for its destructiveness in the past. The effort of our government to preserve the few remaining whooping cranes has also been termed the most sustained and wholehearted it has ever undertaken; the epitome of modern conservation. Because I am a member of that ever-widening group of people who hope that we shall somehow learn to share our planet with other forms of life, and because I am often curious about the substance of the symbols that guide our thoughts, I decided that I should like to know more about the whooping crane.

There was still another reason to be curious about this particular bird. It is almost thirty years—I had often read—since we first began to try to save the whooping crane from extinction, and still we have not definitely succeeded. This struck me as both paradoxical and ominous. The paradox seemed to be that as we become more powerful, we more often find ourselves able to do things that we cannot undo. How was it possible, I wondered, that we could sincerely wish to restore the whooping crane and not be able to accomplish it? How could All the King's Horses and All the King's Men toil so long at this straightforward task and achieve so little? I determined to find out more about the cranes—not only as symbols but also as live creatures—and especially to seek the reason for what appeared to be their uncooperative, even defiant, response to our effort to keep them on earth.

My first inquiries made it clear that the answer was not to be found in any one place, but must be sought in a number of areas and from an unexpectedly varied cast of characters. In one way or another an astonishing number of people have become concerned, in some cases embroiled, in the fate of the cranes. Nor was it possible to understand the birds' present situation without looking into their past. What I have attempted, then, is to reconstruct the chronicle of the cranes year by year since they became officially wards of our government.

At the center of the stage are the whooping cranes themselves. In November, 1965, an annual autumn census showed that there were forty-four wild whooping cranes, thirty-six of them adults and eight young of the year. Compared to many previous autumns, this was a splendidly large number, but compared to the number that would be biologically safe it was perilously small. These birds, the only wild whooping cranes on earth, spend their winters stalking regally about the sand flats and shallow waters of the Aransas Wildlife Refuge, which occupies a small peninsula on the Gulf Coast of Texas, seventy-five miles north of Corpus Christi. Each autumn whooping cranes arrive here, not in a flock but singly or in family groups, during October and November, and settle down on the marshes along the shore. Even from a distance their tall, gleaming white forms are easily seen against the pale yellows of salt grass and sand.

During the quiet months of winter the birds, with the young of the past summer still at their parents' sides, gather strength for the effort ahead; a flight of more than twenty-five hundred miles to northern breeding grounds, and the production of a new generation. In midwinter pairs of birds begin prenuptial dances of a particularly elaborate sort. Then, in April, family by family, or sometimes several families together, the whooping cranes begin their extraordinary and hazardous flight to their nesting grounds.

For years the cranes' destination was one of the most tantalizing of ornithological mysteries. In the words of one baffled observer, "It was as though they flew north each spring and vanished from the face of the

The whooping crane is our tallest bird. An adult is over four feet tall. This one was photographed recently at the Aransas National Wildlife Refuge.

earth." Now, for better or worse, their secret nesting place has been discovered in a far northern corner of Canada's Northwest Territories, within five hundred miles of the Arctic Circle. Summer there is short and capriciously variable. The birds must nest and rear their young on a tight schedule. Any that are delayed even a few weeks will perish in the sudden cold of autumn. In late September the cranes and their newly fledged young begin the return trip to Texas. In the autumn the long flight over Canada and the central United States is even more perilous than in spring, for in the hunting season lakes and marshes, the natural resting places of cranes, are ringed with guns. Rarely in the past thirty years have all the whooping cranes made the round trip without apparent loss—and even then young birds whose existence had not yet been recorded may have been shot between Canada and Texas.

In addition to this group of wild birds there were, in the fall of 1965, seven captive whooping cranes. One of them, a young male named Canus (derived from "Canada" and "U.S."), was injured on the wilderness nesting ground in the summer of 1964 and rescued by helicopter. It is now in the custody of the United States Government, and there is every reason to hope that it will grow to a healthy maturity. The six other captive whooping cranes are currently housed at the Audubon Park Zoo in New Orleans.

The Audubon Park Zoo and the National Audubon Society are both named after the great naturalist, and both are involved in the history of whooping cranes, but they are in no other way connected. The society was founded in 1905 for the purpose of saving endangered wildlife, and is supported by the contributions of its members. The zoo, whose funds come from the city of New Orleans, is managed by civic officials as part of the city's Park Department. Its primary purpose is to provide recreation for New Orleans' citizens. Tropical verdancy, an air of shabby ease, old buildings of pink brick—all make it a pleasant place for a Sunday stroll; but its lack of trained staff or special facilities make it an unlikely site for a crucial experiment in aviculture. Nevertheless, it was here that fate chose to deposit a whooping crane named Josephine who deserves to be known in the annals as the "Dowager Queen of Cranes."

For sixteen years, until her sudden, tragic death in September, 1965, Josephine, the only breeding female crane in captivity, laid eggs that were almost literally worth their weight in gold. With the help of her mate, a splendid old bird named Crip, Josephine laid fifty-two eggs at the Audubon Park Zoo. Twelve of these eggs hatched live young whooping cranes of which four have lived to maturity. In addition to Crip and these surviving young there is a female named Rosie whose procreative capacities have not yet been fully tested. For nine years Rosie, who, like Crip, is the property of the United States Government, idled away her time in sterile captivity at the San Antonio Zoo, which possessed no male whooping crane with which to mate her. In the spring of 1964 Rosie was moved to join the others at Audubon Park in the hope that she might take the torch from the aging Josephine.

During the years that Josephine and Crip labored to preserve their species, the scene at New Orleans was dominated by a man named

George Douglass, who was superintendent of the zoo from 1941 until his death in November, 1964. Douglass's monopoly of the world's supply of captive whooping cranes, coupled with the meager production of young, was a source of embitterment to a variety of people. Although united in little else, Douglass's critics were unanimous in feeling that his most outstanding zoological skill was his ability to hang onto a whooping crane once he got his hands on it. The situation at New Orleans, combined with the ever-imperiled condition of the wild whooping cranes, brought into head-on collision two groups of people, both passionate about whooping cranes and passionately opposed to each other on the question of how to preserve them.

One group is composed of people who have, for many years, believed that the species could be saved from extinction only by breeding whooping cranes in captivity. They argued that offspring from this flock might later be turned loose, or, if this proved unfeasible, there would at least be representatives of the species safely tucked away in zoos and aviaries. The proponents of this plan included men of a variety of backgrounds, ranging from backyard duck breeders to distinguished museum directors, loosely organized under the banner of aviculture—the science of breeding birds in captivity. The initial step would be, of course, to capture a number of wild whooping cranes or take their eggs for artificial incubation.

Opponents of this plan, chiefly the National Audubon Society and its friends, felt that the helping hand of aviculture, if allowed to meddle with the cranes in the fashion proposed, would quite likely finish off the wild flock then and there. The society's biologists pointed out that the capture of large wild birds inevitably involves a high percentage of accidental death or injury. The loss to the cranes of those captured, plus those injured or dispersed, could be a deathblow, reducing the flock below any chance of regeneration. Was it worth such a risk, they asked, in order to attempt breeding experiments whose success could by no means be guaranteed?

A corollary point of disagreement was the tricky biological question of whether there could be any hope of releasing zoo-bred whooping cranes, either to rejoin the wild group or to establish a new wild population. Anyone thinking of the English sparrow and the starling might assume that this would be a simple matter of opening the door of the cage and wishing the whooper Godspeed. Unfortunately, previous experiments with other large, slow-maturing birds have indicated that there are many problems involved in returning captives to the wild. In the case of the cranes, these might or might not be soluble. Thus the argument between those in favor of capturing cranes and those against it approached the philosophical question of the difference in value between wild birds and birds in perpetual captivity.

As the National Audubon Society saw its mission, it was to protect creatures in their natural state, not to provide breeding stock for zoos. In their view a caged and pinioned whooping crane is simply another form of fancy poultry, an ornamental shell representing its once-proud but vanquished race. Thus, if the wild birds perish, the whooping crane will, in any real sense, have become extinct. To this the aviculturists retorted simply that the species would be better off in zoos than in oblivion.

Of the people concerned in the whooping crane's plight, the National Audubon Society is the earliest on the scene, the most dedicated and the most idealistic. It has been able to point out that the only serious research on the natural history of the whooping cranes was the result of its interest and sponsorship.

This study was the work of Robert Porter Allen, who was Research Director of the National Audubon Society. His monograph *The Whooping Crane*, published by the National Audubon Society in 1952, is considered a classic of wildlife research. Until then no accurate information on the natural history of the whooping crane existed. The habits of the species, its diet, nesting, relationship to its habitat, and dozens of other factors bearing on its survival, were all unknown.

Allen dedicated himself heart and soul to finding the answers to such questions. He combed libraries for historical records of whooping cranes. He struggled through the mud of the Texas salt flats to stalk the wintering birds. In summer he flew several hundred thousand miles searching for the mysterious nesting places. In the course of this work Allen became a passionate champion of the whooping cranes. He not only knew more about them than anyone had before him; he also cared more about them than anyone now alive. It is typical of the bad luck that besets the whooping cranes that they lost such a friend. Allen died suddenly in June, 1963.

Ultimately, any decision affecting the wild whooping cranes is made neither by their avicultural friends nor by the National Audubon Society, but by officials of the United States and Canadian Wildlife services. In the United States it is the Bureau of Sport Fisheries and Wildlife, a subdivision of the Fish and Wildlife Service, that is specifically in charge. Even without the problem of whooping cranes on its hands, the bureau would have plenty to worry about. It is perpetually short of the funds to carry out its plans, and equally short of the prestige needed to wage its battles. It has little appeal for voters and hence for congressmen. On the contrary, its mandate to conserve natural habitat for wildlife constantly runs afoul of local economic interests. There are also well-financed and highly organized sportsmen's organizations that see the bureau's primary duty as the provision of game animals. Cattlemen and farmers urge it to concentrate on controlling pests. Conservationists implore it to hold the line. Thus the officials of the bureau, so often beleaguered, are accustomed to compromise as a way of life. It was therefore no novelty for them when the problem of the whooping crane—and how to preserve it—grew ever thornier as the birds' fate aroused ever wider interest. It was clear that if the whooping crane became extinct as the result either of something the bureau did—or left undone—there would be not only tremendous regret among conservationists but also recrimination from those whose advice had gone unheeded.

For almost a decade the bureau wavered between the opposing forces. Only recently has it developed, slowly and painfully, a program for the whooping crane that gives promise of combining the best features of the many solutions that have been offered. In the meantime the existence of the whooping cranes remains precarious. No one knows what the outcome will be. The fate of the species has been delicately balanced for a long, long time. Now the only thing that seems certain is that there will be decisive events and that they will occur comparatively soon.

When I saw my first whooping crane, it was accompanied appropriately enough by a large placard that bore, in red capital letters, the word EXTINCTION. The bird was stuffed, and it stood, looking tall and surprised, one foot lifted and its extraordinary neck in a proud arch, in a glass case in the Natural History Section of the Smithsonian Institution in Washington. This was Exhibit Number 27, dedicated to a few of the birds that are going or recently gone.

"Extinction," the placard continued, "is the dying out of a species. While this has happened to countless thousands of kinds of animals and plants throughout the ages, here we are concerned only with those birds that have disappeared within the memory of man, as well as some others that are now so reduced in numbers as to be in danger of doing so. Directly, by hunting, or indirectly, by virtue of the changes he has wrought on the earth's surface, man is today the chief factor in extermination."

Beside the whooping crane in the case were other birds whose rigid attitudes seemed extraordinarily eloquent of personality. The brown and buff Labrador duck (this one a female; last known specimen collected December 12, 1878) had a rounded, turned-up bill, half open, that made its expression oddly beseeching. The condor, perched on a branch, a huge, dark bird, majestically unattractive, looked as though it would go down to oblivion grandly, scornfully, disdaining any appeal.

At the bottom of the case, appearing to step busily through the artificial leaves and grass, were two little heath hens, their heads inclined toward each other as though nodding in sociable chat. Their smartly barred feathers of russet brown covered plump figures that made me think of Victorian ladies in a fashion book, tripping innocently along to some gay event. The death of the last heath hen was announced on April 21, 1933.

I stared in some disbelief at the great auk, or garefowl, a tall, flightless bird not unlike a penguin, but with an improbable noselike beak. It might have said, "I am not beautiful, but I am me!" Later I read an account of how the last great auk met its death on a tiny island off the coast of Iceland on the morning of June 3, 1844. For hundreds of years these birds, which once lived in multitudes on the coasts and islands of the North Atlantic, had been slaughtered in their rookeries by sailors from passing ships. By 1840 the North American rookeries were empty. Suddenly museum directors awoke to the fact that there were few skins or eggs in their collections. They offered large sums to fishermen to raid the remote, rocky islets on which a few survivors still nested and raised young. After several raids a few dead birds and eggs were brought back, and then the fishermen reported they could find no more garefowl. The museums, still unsatisfied, raised the price even higher. At last a man named Vilhjalmur Hakonarsson agreed to make one more search on the tiny island of Eldey where some birds might have escaped previous raids. The scene on the island was later described by an ornithologist, Seimington Grieve:

"As the men clambered up they saw two garefowl sitting among numberless other rock-birds and at once they gave chase. The garefowl showed not the slightest disposition to repel the invaders, but immediately ran along under the high cliff, their heads erect, their little wings somewhat extended. They uttered no cry of alarm, and moved, with their short steps, about as quickly as a man could walk. Jon Brandsson, with outstretched arms, drove one into a corner, where he soon had it fast. Sigurd Islefsson and Ketil Kentilsson pursued the second, and the former seized it close to the edge of the rock, here risen to a precipice some fathoms high, the water lying directly below. Ketil then returned to the sloping shelf whence the birds had started, and saw an egg lying on the lava slab, which he knew to be a garefowl's. Whether there was not another egg is uncertain. All this took place in much less time than it takes to tell it."

A second later the men had wrung the necks of the two birds and flung their bodies into the boat. Ketil threw the egg away because it showed a tiny crack. At that moment the great auk became extinct.

I turned away from the great auk in the case at the museum to look at a display of Carolina parakeets, small, cheerful-looking green birds with yellow heads and curved beaks. There were sixteen of them placed in a lifelike tableau on branches against a painted snow scene. The clever arrangement gave a feeling of arrested motion, as though a movie projector had been stopped on a still picture. At any moment, I felt, the film might start again and the birds break out of their frozen postures and resume hopping and fluttering and talking among the branches.

In 1881, an ornithologist wrote of the parakeets: "Their enemies are legion; bird catchers trap them by the hundreds for the northern markets, sportsmen shoot them for food, planters kill them because they eat their fruit, and tourists slaughter them simply because they present a favorable mark." The last reported Carolina parakeet was seen in 1904 by Dr. Frank Chapman in a remote swamp in Florida.

In the next case nine beautiful passenger pigeons were placed as though roosting on an oak branch, their necks curved toward each other in graceful bows. A painted backdrop suggested that in the distance were flocks so large they darkened the sky.

The story of the pigeons has been told often, but I find their extermination involves such astonishing figures that they are hard to grasp. From the 1850's until the end, slaughtering pigeons for market was an industry that involved thousands of people, hundreds of thousands of dollars, and billions of birds.

Killing reached such efficiency that it took only a short time to destroy the flocks utterly. The pigeons vanished very quickly between 1870 and 1880. By 1890 there were only a few captive birds in zoos. Suddenly, to everyone's surprise, it became apparent that there was only one. It lived for quite a few years in the Cincinnati Zoological Gardens. This very last bird happens to be in the same case in the Smithsonian as the whooping crane and the others that I looked at that day. It is accompanied by a note: "Martha, the last of her species, died at 1 P.M. September 1, 1914, aged 29."

I came away thinking that the extinction of a species, no matter how alien to us the creature may be, is an awesome thing. In its presence we experience a sort of shiver, perhaps an instinctive (should I say premonitory?) awareness that this is a death quite different from the death of an individual; that it has a different finality. This extinction of something that will never, in all eternity, be duplicated, is an occurrence that seems to break a strand of time itself.

Theodore Roosevelt wrote: "The destruction of the wild pigeon and the Carolina Paroquet has meant a loss as severe as if the Catskills or the Palisades were taken away. When I hear of the destruction of a species I feel just as if all the works of some great writer had perished; as if we had lost all, instead of only part, of Polybius or Livy." I think of these words when I hear people ask why there is so much fuss about wildlife, such as whooping cranes—or whenever I wonder myself why it seems worthwhile to document the crucial and possibly final years on earth of a small band of white birds.

2

Although the whooping crane is the tallest North American bird, it is not mere size, but something that can best be described as total personality that makes it so striking and impressive a creature. An adult male whooper weighs perhaps twenty to twenty-five pounds, and stands a little over four feet tall. Its height is in the long, delicate legs and agile neck, longer and more sinuous than that of a swan, to which the long spear-shaped bill is in elegant proportion. Its tapered white body is poised on its black legs in an almost upright fashion, so that the bird's silhouette is something like that of a man in a swallowtail coat. At rest the bird appears pure white except for a ruby crown and cheek patches that are, in fact, red skin bare of feathers, and a mask of glistening black featherlets that ends in points on its cheeks, suggesting a Victorian moustache of the fiercer sort. When the crane's wings are spread to their astonishing breadth of seven and a half feet, it can be seen that the wing tips are satiny black. The innermost flight feathers, the tertials, are white, and longer than the primaries. Allen describes them as "exquisite and plumelike." Curving backward, they trail over the edges of the folded wings, hiding the black tips; or, if the bird desires, it can raise these plumes over its back in display. Except when the whooping crane is feeding, it holds its narrow, patrician head high. The color of its eyes is a cold, frosty yellow. The bird has an alert, farsighted gaze that seems to scan distant horizons with a fierce, wild recognition of some primeval challenge invisible to human beings. At least, that is the sort of notion that the whooping crane is able to inspire.

The female whooping crane is outwardly identical with the male (which adds a baffling factor to the problem of crane "management," as the professionals term human attempts to interfere in the private affairs of wild creatures), except that she is a trifle smaller and her demeanor gentler (Allen called it "more domestic"), while her mate's is heavily masculine. The difference, however, is obvious only when the birds are a mated pair.

In flight, whooping cranes are fully as regal as they are on the ground.

After watching the cranes in Texas, at the Aransas Refuge, Allen wrote:

"The sight of a Whooping Crane in the air is an experience packed with beauty and drama. We see the broad sweep of the great wings in their stiff, almost ponderous motion, the flash of sunlight on the satin white plumage. As we drive down the narrow trail that borders the low salt flats a trio of the big fellows may appear, quite suddenly, in the waist-high oak brush, where they have been feeding on acorns. Their heads come up and the shrill, bugle-like notes send a shiver along your spine. They are up at once, leaning forward, running a few steps and then lifting their heavy bodies in straight-away, horizontal flight. Neck and head are extended forward, like a spear or lance, and slightly down. The long black legs stretch out behind. The wing stroke is like that of the other cranes, and of the limpkins as well. The complete arc of the stroke is narrow and there is a powerful *flick* on the upbeat. Normal flight produces about two beats to the second and there is ease and competence in the way these giants skim low over the salt grass towards the shore of the bay.

"In the grim aspect of the features, in the whole trim of the birds as they move, silently now, there is a dignity and a sense of unconquered wildness, of an obstinate will to survive. We watch them with admiration and with hope. In spite of its glowing reality, it is like a brief and unexpected look at the World as it was in the beginning."

Earlier writers have described a spectacle that nowadays no more than a handful of people are in a position to witness—an aerial ballet of whooping cranes high in the sky, an exercise the birds may indulge in just before and during migration. In a book entitled *Our Feathered Game,* published in 1911, the author, Dwight W. Huntington, tells of watching a flock of migrating whooping cranes rise from a marsh: "When quite overhead in the azure sky, their white feathers gleaming in the sunlight, they proceeded to go through many graceful evolutions, flying about in a circle, forming sides and crossing over and back and dancing in midair to their own loud music."

Yet whooping cranes are great walkers as well as flyers. In the winter months at Aransas they walk more than they fly. But "walk" is not a properly important word to describe the gait of a whooping crane. The bird moves with a peculiar, stately step, marked by a tiny pause just before the lifting of each foot. It brings to mind solemn human ceremonies, clerical processions and the aisle of Westminster Abbey.

The mighty voice that gives the crane its name is produced from a trachea five feet long coiled like a French horn inside the breastbone. The sound has been variously described as a whoop, a bugle call, or a trumpet sound. The whooping crane can modulate its voice through a fairly extensive vocabulary of sound. Both sexes trumpet when they are disturbed, angry, or wish to threaten an intruder. Under the right conditions the whoop can be heard for a mile or more. Probably the cranes sometimes whoop just for the joy of it. Or did. So few people have heard them lately that old sources are the best witness. In 1883 *Forest and Stream* published this account:

"In fine, calm weather he (the Whooping Crane) delights to mount up, in great, undulating spirals, to the height of a mile or so, and take a quiet float, while he whoops at neighbors in the adjoining counties.

"After airing himself to his heart's content, he descends, sometimes spirally as he rose, at other times with great plunges and wild, reckless dives, until within about 50 feet of the earth when he hangs himself upon the air, with his long, spindling legs down, gently settles and alights."

Whooping cranes mate for life. In the wild, family ties are very strong; so much so that if one member is shot the others remain close to the wounded or dead bird, and thus they, too, are exposed to danger. Parent cranes share the month-long job of incubating the eggs—only two are laid in a setting—and later share the care and defense of the young. A newly hatched whooping crane is no more than half the size of a full-grown robin. It is covered with soft, reddish down. It spends its first days within the warmth of its parents' feathers, but then can run about, following the older cranes as they search for food. By the time the young whooping cranes start the southern flight from Canada to the Aransas Refuge in the autumn, they are nearly five months old. The plumage of immature birds is not white, but a calico mixture of grayish whites and brownish reds. At a distance they look almost pink. Unknowing hunters can easily mistake them for some other sort of bird, particularly when the whooping cranes are feeding with their grayish cousins, the sandhill cranes; and so the coloration of the immature birds adds yet another hazard to the fall migration.

The scientific name of the whooping crane is *Grus americana*. Cranes, members of the Order Gruiformes, which includes other cranelike birds—rails, coots, gallinules, sun grebes, sun bitterns—are quite high on the evolutionary scale by which birds are classified. They rank above the herons (with which laymen often confuse them), above swans, geese, ducks, hawks, grouse, and quail, and just below the plovers and their relatives. It is in Asia that crane species are most abundant. Of the twenty-three species and subspecies of cranes now living, eight are native to Asia. They are the birds whose gracefully curving forms appear so often in Oriental art. South America is the only continent that has no cranes. North America has two species, the whooping crane and the sandhill crane, *Grus canadensis*. Sandhills are divided into four races, forms that do not differ enough to be termed distinct species, but are still distinguishable. All four are smaller than whooping cranes, and their plumage is predominantly gray. Unlike whoopers, sandhills are gregarious birds, and much less demanding of special habitat. As a result fairly large numbers of sandhills survive quite nicely in conditions that their inflexible cousins cannot tolerate.

Grus americana probably evolved from marsh-dwelling ancestors during the Pleistocene period, some 500,000 years ago, a time when the vast prairies, inland seas, and wet savannas of our continent presented a quite different landscape from that of today. After the withdrawal of the last glacier, during the long period when grass was the predominant vegetation, the cranes increased to their maximum numbers. Fossil bones show that in this, their Golden Age, whooping cranes ranged from coast to coast and from the arctic to central Mexico. In time, however, forests emerged to encroach on the grasslands, the water table subsided, and a relentless shrinking of crane habitat began. It was probably then that the sandhill crane adapted itself to a less watery world while the whooping crane, victim of what has been called "crystallized psychology," and unable to change its habits, stayed within ever-narrowing confines. Imprisoned by this need for a land like that which gave it birth, a land of shallow waters, and vast seas of grassy, marsh vegetation, the whooping crane retreated in numbers as well as range. Robert Allen believed that even before there was significant human interference the whooping-crane population had shrunk to no more than fifteen hundred birds.

These birds were never a single flock, and claimed no single area as their home. Rather they could be found wherever there was the proper combination of water and vegetation. On the East Coast whooping cranes wintered on the Atlantic shore from the Carolinas to New Jersey. But by far the greatest wintering ground for cranes was in southwestern Louisiana where, until settlers arrived, there were two million acres of tall-grass prairie ideal for whoopers.

Also resident in southwestern Louisiana was a peculiar group of whooping cranes that for some reason did not migrate, but nested in the same area in which it wintered. Allen speculated that these birds might be the descendants of a group that formed this nonmigratory habit during a prehistoric period when glaciation forced all the cranes to nest far to the south of their later breeding grounds, and had, for some reason, clung to it ever after.

A remnant of this tribe survived until recent times, hidden in a sort of watery version of Conan Doyle's Lost World. This was a marsh of forty thousand acres of yellow grass, or "paille fine," as the Cajuns call it, near White Lake, Louisiana. There were a goodly number in the colony until about 1900, when hunting had so reduced it that the remaining birds, which had retreated to inaccessible portions of the marsh, were forgotten by the outside world. Then in 1929, the United States Army Engineers, in the course of their ceaseless improvements, extended the Intracoastal Waterway from the Vermilion River to Grand Lake.

The whooping crane belongs in a world of marsh and shallow water. Small marine creatures are its staple food.

As they drove through the marsh, they incidentally "rediscovered" the lost colony of cranes.

Although Louisiana was the heartland of the migratory cranes' winter territory, the species was by no means confined to it. Other whooping cranes, in lesser numbers than the Louisiana population of migrant whoopers, spent their winters patrolling the sea-rim marshes of the Gulf of Mexico, from New Orleans to the Rio Grande Delta. In the interior grasslands of Texas and northern Mexico there were also scattered sites where lakes and marshes once provided good whooping-crane habitat. Propably the whooping cranes of different localities did not mix, and met only accidentally when migration paths converged. For generation after generation individual whooping cranes remained bound by racial memory to the territories of their ancestors both in winter and in summer.

The original breeding grounds of the cranes ranged from the prairies of the central United States on up through Canada to the point beyond which severe weather made it impossible to rear young.

Allen wrote that "its preferred niche, especially when nesting, is a flat, or slightly rolling, open area interspersed with bulrush, cattail and sedge marshes and swales, covered with standing water and having the biotic characteristics found in the willow communities of the aspen parkland. There must be a great abundance of small animal life, including basic invertebrate forms. The entire area must be several hundred (or even several thousand) acres in size and completely isolated from human disturbance of any sort."

It is hard for us to realize now that less than a hundred years ago the lush prairies that then stretched from central Illinois westward across northern Iowa, western Minnesota, and eastern North Dakota fitted this description. Best of all whooper nesting habitat, and the heart of their nesting area, was the prairie of northern Iowa. An ornithologist, J. W. Preston, wrote a description of the marshes at the headwaters of the Iowa River that gives a picture of this general habitat:

"Years ago, when northwestern Iowa was a vast prairie, out onto which few settlers had ventured and the monotony was seldom broken save by some wood-fringed lake or a herder's shanty . . . my way lay along the Iowa River, from the headwaters of which stream, westward, was a great, flat prairie, interspersed with marshes and small lakes, about which swarmed countless numbers of shore birds. . . ."

Preston, in search of eggs, reached a marsh where whooping cranes were nesting: His notes bear witness to the comparative rarity of the birds even then, in the 1880's:

"Pond and shallow water, overgrown with rushes, stretched for miles with occasional tracts of tussocks. Among these I wandered about, getting sight of a pair of Geese here, a frightened Rail there. Occasionally a flock of Sand-peeps whistled by me. Hours passed away, and when I was turning campward I caught sight of the snowy forms of a pair of White Cranes flying slowly toward me."

The nest grounds of the whooping cranes were connected with their winter homes by more or less fixed pathways of migration. Birds from the Louisiana area flew north to their nest sites in Illinois, Iowa, Minnesota, and eastern North Dakota. Texas migrants converged at the Platte River in Nebraska, and then, after following the river for a time, spread out to nesting grounds in the northern United States and Canada.

Even in migration whooping cranes never formed flocks in the sense that more social birds do. Early records describe migrant groups as numbering ten to twenty birds; on rare occasions as many as thirty or forty were sighted at one time. The Platte River was (and remains) a major resting place on the migration route where the birds might come to earth and stay for several days. Allen found old-timers who recalled seeing the great white forms of whoopers dotting the sandbars in the river at nightfall. There were still a few buffalo on the plains, and in the morning the whooping cranes moved to the riverbanks to hunt for insects and frogs in the buffalo wallows or to stalk grasshoppers through the open grassy stretches.

When the cranes were ready to resume their journey, usually in the afternoon, they would gather together, then rise and circle higher and higher until, as one old man said to Allen, "they found the right air current." The old man remembered how the great birds could be heard calling to one another as they disappeared into the depths of the sky.

3

For a good many thousands of years whooping cranes ranged a continent as yet untroubled by the advent of human beings. In that time layers of ice stretched out and receded; mountains moved, and new shores rose out of the seas. Finally the first human beings entered the hemisphere from Asia, and spread to its farthest extremity. But *Grus americana,* as Allen wrote, "unchanged, moved through these shifting scenes with the same nobility, the same dignity we know today. After unknown generations of existence, the drama—the tragic drama—of its meeting with 'civilized' man—was about to unfold."

Nobody knows which of the several accounts by early explorers of North America that speak of "cranes" deserves the honor of being considered the first written record of that meeting. For instance, Captain Luke Fox, who visited Hudson Bay in 1631, wrote that there was brought on board his ship "two goodly Swannes, and a young Tall Fowle alive; it was long-headed, long-neckt, and a body almost unanswerable. I could not discerne whether it was an Estridge or no, for it was but penfeathered. Within 3 or 4 dayes, the legges by mischance were broken and it dyed."

This could have been a sandhill crane or, just as easily, a whooping crane. Other accounts are similarly ambiguous until we come to that of Mark Catesby, an English naturalist, who visited South Carolina in 1722. During his travels along the coast, an Indian presented him with a skin that Catesby realized belonged to a hitherto undescribed species of bird. He recorded it in his *Natural History* as *Grus americana alba.* Twenty-two years later the whooping crane was mentioned again, this time by a French explorer in Canada who, in 1744, wrote with an accuracy uncharacteristic of whooping-crane annals: "We have [in Canada] cranes of two colors; some are all white, the others pale grey, all make excellent soup." Then, in 1748, a certain Mr. Isham brought a dried whooping-crane skin from Hudson Bay to London and gave it to George Edwards, author of *A Natural History of Birds the Most of Which Have Not Hitherto Been Figured or Described,* who described it therein. In 1770 these sketchy references to *Grus americana* were amplified by the explorer Samuel Hearne, again with an accuracy that was to become increasingly rare: "This bird visits Hudson's Bay in the Spring, though not in great numbers. They are generally seen only in pairs, and that not very often. . . . It is esteemed good eating. The wing-bones of this bird are so long and large, that I have known them made into flutes. . . ."

Thereafter, for many years, even though the continent was increasingly explored, the written record of whooping cranes remained meager and frequently misleading. Audubon painted a whooping crane at New Orleans in 1821, but his notes show that he confused it with the sandhill. So, most probably, did an English botanist named Thomas Nuttall, who, while "leisurely descending on the bosom of the Mississippi" in 1811, saw what he took to be a vast migration of whooping cranes passing overhead "in such legions" that their "deafening clangor" continued throughout the whole night. Nuttall further described roosting flocks of whooping cranes emitting "clamorous cries . . . braying tones . . . jingling and trumpeting hurrahs." Allen, obviously affronted by such an insulting description of *Grus americana,* wrote that in the first instance Nuttall probably witnessed a sandhill migration and in the second must have "stumbled upon a hidden corral full of jackasses," since whooping cranes could not conceivably utter such sounds. Nuttall's errors, however, were not so clear to the ornithologists immediately succeeding him. His remarks about "migratory hosts" were preferred to less flamboyant testimony on the scarceness of whooping cranes, and have continued to be quoted, to support a widespread myth that whooping cranes were once as numerous as buffalo, right down to the present.

The period around 1850 was a turning point in the history of the whooping crane. Until then the sparse settlement of the land west of the Mississippi posed no serious threat to crane habitat. Suddenly, changes that had been in the making for fifty years seemed almost to explode. Economic and political events had sent a great tide of settlers westward. Railroad surveys opened up virgin land. Canada was rapidly explored. The Northwest Territories from the Great Lakes to Tennessee had become part of the Union in 1819, and thereafter were steadily settled and civilized. The Southwest, Louisiana, Texas, the Oregon Territory, all were opened up during the extraordinary first fifty years of the century.

In 1858, it occurred to Dr. Spencer Fullerton Baird, a leading ornithologist of the day, that the whooping crane had been scientifically neglected. He wrote: "The *Grus americanus,* though common in Texas and Florida, is yet one of the rarest birds in collections. There are none in any of the public museums of the United States, as far as I have been able to ascertain."

Baird's errors (*Grus americana* was common nowhere, and nonexistent in Florida) reflect the scientific ignorance of which Baird himself complained. It was indeed true that the whooping crane, because it was comparatively so rare, had been barely described. In 1858, its life history,

Audubon painted a whooping crane at New Orleans in 1821, but his notes confused it with the sandhill crane.

its numbers, even its true range were still unknown. Ironically, it was not until thirty years later, when the crane population was melting like snow, that ornithologists began recording accurate information about the species.

Dr. Baird obtained a whooping-crane skin, which he presented to the United States National Museum, where it still resides as catalogue item No. 10384. As though mobilized by Dr. Baird's remarks, collectors became eager for whooping-crane skins and eggs. These trophies became increasingly valuable. In 1887, whooping-crane skins went for $2.50 each, or at the wholesale rate of $2.00 if purchased in lots of one dozen or more. Only three years later, skins were sold at $8.00 to $18.00, depending on their condition. At first, eggs could be had for as little as $0.50 each. By 1890, they had risen to $2.00 each.

It is probable that 90 percent of the whooping-crane population disappeared in the thirty years between 1870 and 1900. No single human activity was to blame for the loss. Almost every change that occurred was inimical to the species: agriculture, drainage, cattle, settlement, hunting, even egg collecting—all were interwoven in their destruction.

The first to go, and numerically the biggest loss, were the whooping cranes that wintered on the Louisiana prairies and nested in the north-central states, for these were attacked on both winter and summer territory. Settlers came into northwestern Louisiana in the early 1800's. Undoubtedly they shot whooping cranes wherever they found them. Grus gumbo must have been a tempting dish. But it was the introduction of rice as a major crop in the 1880's that suddenly changed the face of the southern prairie. Within a few years millions of acres of grassland were turned to rice fields.

The last record of migratory whooping cranes in what was once the heart of their winter kingdom is of an incident on the prairie above Sweet Lake in 1918, when a farmer named Alcie Daigle shot twelve whooping cranes that were feeding on rice fallen from his threshing machine.

While rice farmers were taking over the whooping cranes' Louisiana wintering grounds, other settlers were moving into their summer territory in Iowa, Minnesota, North Dakota, and Illinois. The wild, wide spaces became wheat fields, homesteads, and cattle ranches. Streams were diverted and marshes drained. By 1880, whooping cranes no longer nested in Illinois. Nesting birds had disappeared from North Dakota by 1884, and the last Minnesota eggs were collected in 1889. On May 26, 1894, an ornithologist named Rudolph M. Anderson searched a marsh near Eagle Lake, Hancock County, Iowa, where crane eggs had been collected in the past. He sighted a pair of whooping cranes that "rose with slow, heavy flaps of their great wings," and moved to the far side of the marsh. There they stalked along with "long strides, as fast as a man could walk." They bugled protestingly, but did not defend their nest. This was the last wild pair found nesting in the United States.

In Canada the known nesting places of the cranes lasted a little longer. Then, on May 28, 1922, at a place unromantically known as Muddy Lake, Saskatchewan, a game warden named Fred Bradshaw came upon a pair of nesting whooping cranes. He later told how the birds attempted to lead him away, one bird circling within a hundred yards of him while he photographed the nest.

Then Bradshaw heard a "strange, piping whistle," which he discovered to be the cry of an infant whooping crane, just broken from the shell. He seized it easily and deftly wrung its neck, in order, as Allen wrote, "to efficiently collect this uttermost nib of surviving offspring and give it immortality in the form of a tag with a number on it." The chick is No. 30393 in the Royal Museum in Toronto. This was the last live whooping crane nestling that anyone would see, in the wild, for over thirty years. Until the discovery of the one remaining wilderness breeding ground of the whooping cranes, in 1955, it seemed that it might be the last ever to be seen. Meanwhile, in 1946, in the first phase of the long search for the hidden nests of the cranes, one of the searchers flew over Muddy Lake in an airplane. He found the lake as dry as dust.

Today, of course, almost all the United States and Canadian nesting sites accessible to man have been changed beyond recognition. Some that were marshes are now dry land. Others have become summer resorts, farms, towns, or the environs of towns; dumps, wrecked-car lots, gravel pits, and such. In just a few spots, which have not been attractive to development, there are still water, food, and isolation. These places still shelter nesting ducks, but no whooping cranes nest there.

In Texas the destruction of the habitat of the whooping crane was neither so sudden nor so simple as in Louisiana, but proceeded as inexorably. The Rio Grande area, once wet enough for cranes, gradually dried up as a result of drainage, farming, and grazing. Overgrazing changed the character of the vegetation and lowered the water table so that once-verdant areas of southern Texas became near desert. Along the coastal strip north from the Mexican border to New Orleans, almost every acre of land has been altered by human use. Marshes have been filled and shallows dredged. At the mouth of the Brazos River whooper territory is now the scene of oil refining, sulfur extraction, and kindred industrial uses. It is as congenial to whooping cranes as the center of Houston, only sixty miles away. The sea-rim marshes of coastal Louisiana have been less dramatically altered, but even so whooping cranes did not survive there. In the 1920's there was a sudden boom in muskrat fur. The price rose to a dollar a pelt. Thousands of trappers came to the marshes between New Orleans and Port Arthur, hastening the end of the small groups of cranes that still wintered there.

Loss of territory was the major reason for the disappearance of the cranes, but it was never the only hazard to them. Another major factor was, and remains, hunting. A whooping crane is an easy target. Its double curse of size and beauty seems especially to arouse the killing instinct in gunners.

Sporting journals of fifty years ago contain enthusiastic descriptions of shooting the "big white fellows." The greatest number were shot during migration, and the heaviest loss was in Nebraska, where the whoopers followed a route that was highly accessible to hunters. The greatest number were killed in the 1890's. After that, the kill record declines as the whooping-crane population declines. Since 1916 and the ratification of the Migratory Bird Treaty between the United States and Great Britain, and hence Canada, it has been illegal to shoot whooping cranes, yet they are still being shot. In the ten years from 1939 to 1948, thirty-nine adult whooping cranes were lost. Allen estimated that less than half died of "natural causes"; the rest were shot on migration. There is no way to know how many juvenile whooping cranes, whose existence had not yet been recorded, died on their maiden trip from their birthplace to Texas.

Egg collecting is no longer a problem for obvious reasons, but there was a time when even this pretty Victorian pastime took a toll. There was a particular vogue for it in the 1880's and 1890's. Ostensibly the object was scientific, but the majority of "eggers" failed to keep records. Of the 121 whooping-crane eggs that Allen was able to find in museums and private collections, hardly any were accompanied by such simple data as time, place, and circumstance of collection, so that the eggs are valueless to the scientist. This dearth Allen ascribed to the "childishly competitive" aspects of egg collecting.

Eggers robbed nests and at the same time blandly deplored the growing scarcity of material. The only legacy of value bequeathed us by the eggers are quaint descriptions of nest sites and the behavior of the nesting birds. Some of these were written with true Victorian sensibility of the pathos of the situation. In 1876, a man named George B. Sennett, an inveterate collector, set out to gather whooping-crane eggs at Elbow Lake, Minnesota. He found a nest built on top of a muskrat house in a marsh. After frightening off the birds he hid himself nearby:

"Fully half an hour went by [Sennet later wrote] . . . when one noble fellow flew over the slough and lit on the opposite shore. Cautiously he began to survey the situation and shortly his mate came swooping down to his side. . . . Some fifteen minutes of strutting back and forth when she boldly walked out into the water, some eight or ten inches deep, directly toward me, mounted the rat house and sat down on her two eggs.

"I could see her wink her eyes, watching me and her mate constantly. Her eyes gleamed like fire. How anxious and how handsome, was ever a sight so grand! The male stood on the ridge watching her closely for a few minutes, when, feeling all was safe he calmly commenced to plume himself in grand style and shortly walked off away from me, the proudest of birds. I slowly arose, turned, and gave her one barrel as she was rising from the nest and the next before she had gone six feet and dropped her in the water."

J. W. Preston, the ornithologist and writer who described the Iowa marshes where the last nest in the United States was found, also did his share of egg collecting. He described how, from a hiding place, he saw a female whooping crane alight and walk into the tall grass that concealed her nest. Preston followed:

"To my delight she was sitting on her heavily marked drab egg, which lay in a neat cavity in the top of a well-built heap of tough, fine marsh grass one and a half feet high on firm sod. The eggs were the first I'd seen and were a rare prize to me. When I approached the nest, the bird, which had walked some distance away, came running back . . . trotting awkwardly around, wings and tail spread drooping, with head and shoulders brought to a level with the water; then it began picking up bunches of moss and sticks which it threw down in a defiant way; then, with pitiable mien, it spread itself upon the water and begged me to leave its treasure, which, in a heartless manner, I did not do."

Fortunately another pastime, more fruitful than egg collecting, was also born in the 1880's, and gave ornithology a new dimension. Bird-watching was virtually invented by Wells B. Cooke, an ornithologist with the Division of Economic Ornithology of the United States Department of Agriculture. Working from his desk in Washington, Cooke organized a vast correspondence soliciting reports on birds from amateurs all over the nation and in Canada. In effect, Cooke mobilized an army of observers; a motley group whose ranks included hunters, housewives, teachers, eggers, farmers, and small boys. The result was a hitherto impossible coverage reaching into the far corners of the country. Cooke's bulletin on migratory birds, published in 1888, was a landmark in whooping-crane history, in that it provided the first reasonably accurate picture of their winter distribution. And just in time: a few years later the birds had disappeared from 90 percent of this range without trace.

Even so, reliable information on the numbers of whoopers was not easily come by. Somehow, perhaps dating back to Nuttall's accounts, there was a fixed belief that whooping cranes had once been abundant, and that "somewhere" they were abundant still. The myth took a long time to die. While some ornithologists were warning that *Grus americana* was alarmingly scarce or possibly already extinct, others maintained that the species was in no danger. This confusion among people who should have known better was typical of the whooping cranes' bad luck, and helped postpone the rescue operation until almost too late.

In 1912, a year when, according to Robert Allen's reconstruction of their history, there were actually eighty to a hundred whooping cranes alive, the bell was tolled by an authority named Edward Howe Forbush, who wrote a history of the game birds of New England. "The whooping crane is doomed to extinction," he declared. "It has disappeared from its former habitat in the east and is now found only in uninhabited places." Dr. William T. Hornaday, of the New York Zoological Park, who had a captive whooping crane for which he had been unable to secure a mate, was ready to concur. "This splendid bird will almost certainly be the next North American species to be totally exterminated," he wrote in 1913. He added that a standing offer of $1,000, made by an English gentleman, for a live pair of whooping cranes had gone unanswered for five years.

At about the same time, a certain Professor Myron H. Swenk, of Lincoln, Nebraska, took a hand in whooping-crane history. An admirer and champion of the birds, his long and patient labors to rally interest in them were neatly canceled by his blunders in appraising their situation. Swenk made, and published, spring and autumn tallies of the number of migrating whooping cranes observed in Nebraska. His mistaken reports of large numbers clouded the truth during the critical decades from 1912 to 1934.

Despite Swenk's optimistic reports, others erred on the darker side. In 1923 the *Saturday Evening Post* published an article by Hal G. Evarts, a popular nature writer, which announced that the whooping crane had already "travelled the long trail to oblivion." Evarts had been given the skin of what he thought was the "last straggler," and presented it to the museum in Yellowstone Park. His account of the trail to extinction included a description of how the whooping cranes were shot year after year as they migrated over a salt marsh near Hutchinson, Kansas. An enterprising resident of the area captured two crippled survivors of the sport and, reportedly, sold them for $1,900 to a dealer in New York who intended to ship them to Australia. Before they could be sent off, the birds died in the Bronx Zoo.

Two years after Evarts wrote their epitaph Dr. Swenk reported a spring flight of sixty-five whooping cranes across the Platte River. This "firsthand" report entered the ornithological literature and tended to lull alarm over the birds' status. It apparently helped to reassure Dr. T. Gilbert Pearson, president of the National Association of Audubon Societies, for in 1932 he told a convention of conservationists that current information from Nebraska showed the cranes to be "somewhat more numerous" than indicated by the gloomy figures previously reported.

In truth, as far as it can be reconstructed, after 1918 there were only three groups of migratory whooping cranes in existence: The King Ranch in Texas was the wintering ground of perhaps sixteen birds; at the site of the present Aransas Refuge on the Blackjack Peninsula there were approximately twenty-five whooping cranes; and on the sea-rim marshes of the Louisiana coast six or eight birds held out during the

1920's. Allen calculated that the grand total for 1918 was forty-seven birds. This figure had probably been somewhat reduced by 1925 when Dr. Swenk made his report of sixty-five migrating whooping cranes.

During this critical period of decline in the fortunes of the cranes, Dr. Swenk continued to be the only person seriously interested in their fate, but unfortunately he remained convinced that the birds were holding their own—or better. In 1933, he wrote that while he didn't want to minimize the danger of their situation he felt that the number of whooping cranes migrating through Nebraska had in fact increased since 1916. Dr. Swenk had come to believe that somewhere there was a great flock of whooping cranes and that the scattered individuals seen in spring and fall were simply wanderers from this flock. He clung to this belief even though, year after year, the "great flock" failed to appear. The truth is that in later years Dr. Swenk was seldom in the field himself. He confused an increase in the number of bird watchers with an increase in the number of whooping cranes. As Swenk's years of devoted missionary work to educate Nebraskans about whooping cranes enlisted a growing army of farmers, hunters, and housewives scanning the skies in the spring and fall, his graph of "whooping cranes" sighted steadily rose. Years later, Robert Allen tracked down similar amateur reports of whooping cranes and found them to be in reality an assortment of pelicans, gulls, sandhills, and snow geese. Undoubtedly Swenk's well-meaning friends made the same mistakes.

Dr. Swenk's miscalculation was almost fatal to the cranes. "On the strength of this rosy picture," Allen wrote, "direct action on their behalf was seriously delayed." Poor Swenk, whose error was born of concern, would have been one of those most grieved had he realized the true situation.

Dr. Swenk's figures were not challenged because no one was in a position to refute them. As late as 1941, the American Ornithologists' Union reported: "Estimates made in 1938 place the whooping crane population at less than three hundred." That estimate was at least technically correct. Allen reconstructed the actual population of 1938 as consisting of eleven birds in the nonmigratory flock at White Lake, Louisiana, and eighteen migratory whooping cranes on the Blackjack Peninsula, Texas.

There were no others. The last of the King Ranch birds had vanished the year before. The last migrants of the Louisiana coastal marshes had perished. There were twenty-nine whooping cranes left on earth. Swenk's great flock was a phantom, and the species itself very nearly one.

At this critical moment, in December, 1937, the United States Biological Survey, forerunner of the Fish and Wildlife Service, made its first move, riding up like a cavalry regiment in a romance of the Old West, just in time to untie the heroine from the railroad tracks.

4

One of the few occasions when an encounter between a man and a whooping crane has been fortunate for the crane occurred in 1936. Early that winter a biologist named Neil Hotchkiss, on a scouting mission for the Bureau of Biological Survey, visited the Blackjack Peninsula and saw four whooping cranes, as well as a fine assortment of water birds. Hotchkiss recorded the cranes in his notes on wildlife observed in the area, and reported to Washington that the peninsula merited further investigation as a possible waterfowl refuge.

A few months later, in the small town of Brady, Nebraska, some thousand miles distant from Texas, one other event important in whooping-crane history took place. It was described thus by the Lincoln County *Tribune*:

> BRADY, NEBRASKA, June 10 (Special to the *Tribune*)—A large white Heron was sighted by the Henry George girls while riding their bicycles Friday and returning to the house with the news, Mr. George took the car and drove the Heron for a mile into a 5-foot wire netting fence where it was caught. It had been shot and one wing and its eye were injured. It easily looked over the fence. It was turned over to the Gothenburg Sanctuary where it was let loose.

The sanctuary was a large pen where the whooping crane lived, one-eyed and unreconciled, refusing to make peace either with its keepers, members of the Gothenburg Gun Club, or with the assorted poultry sharing its quarters, for the next twelve years.

Hotchkiss's visit to Texas had not been accidental. During the 1930's nature and economics, dustbowl and depression suddenly combined in favor of conservation. The depletion of all our natural resources, including wildlife, had become dramatically apparent. At this moment, too, federal funds were flowing. Thanks to the herculean efforts of J. N. ("Ding") Darling, the Iowa cartoonist who had become the crusading

Chief of the Bureau of Biological Survey, Congress for the first time consented to spend sizable amounts on wildlife. The result was a brief Golden Age of acquisition when hundreds of thousands of acres were bought for sanctuaries. The refuge program of the Biological Survey, transfused with money, leaped into life. Biologists were dispatched on survey missions to select the most useful sites from among the scores of possibilities. Thus it happened that Hotchkiss made the difficult trip over the narrow dirt road that led to the last redoubt of the whooping crane.

A short time later Hotchkiss returned with two colleagues; J. Clark Salyer, II, Chief of the Refuge Branch, and George B. Saunders, a Bureau ornithologist. Again whooping cranes were noted. Then Saunders, who had studied the whooping cranes' cousins in Africa as well as in North America, spent several weeks looking over a wide stretch of coast. He saw whooping cranes nowhere but in the Blackjack vicinity, a circumstance that interested him deeply. As a result he recommended the purchase of the Blackjack Peninsula and of the two protective islands of Matagorda and St. Joseph, just off its shores, where he had also seen whoopers.

Adjacent to the land for sale on the Blackjack Peninsula was another tract—the Hallinan Ranch—which, Saunders noted, was an ideal habitat for Attwater's prairie chicken, and so he recommended that also. The answer from Washington was that the Bureau couldn't buy that much territory in one place; if he couldn't have it all, which portion was the most important? Saunders, thinking of the whooping cranes, as well as the waterfowl, replied, "Blackjack." Thus the refuge does not include the islands of Matagorda and St. Joseph, which could have been protective barriers to the privacy of the peninsula. The bureau's decision to eliminate the islands and the Hallinan Ranch was sadder and more consequential than anyone could possibly have known. Not long thereafter the prairie chickens gave up their habitat to large-scale farming. Today the species is high on the danger list.

Nevertheless, it was a crucial moment in whooping-crane history when the bureau decided to purchase the Blackjack Peninsula. There is no reason to doubt that the whooping cranes would otherwise have vanished years ago. The bureau bought 47,261 acres, roughly 74 square miles, for $463,500. On December 31, 1937, President Roosevelt signed an executive order that transformd it into the Aransas Migratory Waterfowl Refuge, a title later transmuted into its present one—the Aransas National Wildlife Refuge.

The entire Gulf coast of Texas is a strategic area for water birds. Its crescent coastline, extending some 360 miles between Louisiana and Mexico, is protected for much of its length by a chain of long, thin, sandy islands that follow the shore like a breakwater. Between the islands and the mainland are shallow lagoons where oyster reefs and marine meadows of seaweed provide splendid feeding grounds for waterfowl.

The Aransas Refuge region has an especially rich variety to offer wildlife. It is part of a peculiar area where it seems land and water have not finally made up their minds to part. Much of the land is as level as the sea itself, and there is a wide, intermediate zone where bays, lagoons, sloughs, and ponds make lacework of the shore. Wide expanses of marsh just barely rise above the water. Like islands in these seas of salt grass

In neutral territory cranes do not dispute the right of others to drink. At left are two sandhill cranes, similar in outline to whooping cranes, but smaller.

are mud flats that are sometimes claimed by the land, sometimes by the water, depending on wind and tide. The tides here are peculiar, too. They do not rise and fall on a predictable, moon-determined schedule, but are influenced by the strong, persistent winds characteristic of these shores, especially in spring and fall. The level of the water may rise, covering the low land, and stay at the flood for days or even weeks. Then, with wind from another direction, the water is blown offshore, out of the ponds and sloughs, and will remain at ebb until the wind changes.

The Blackjack Peninsula, or what has now become the Aransas Refuge, is a thumb of land pointing southwest. It runs almost parallel to the mainland shore, something like the thumb of a man's hand in relation to the other fingers. To the west a sliver of water, St. Charles Bay, separates the peninsula from the mainland. On the east the peninsula is flanked by a long lagoon beyond which the sandbar islands of St. Joseph and Matagorda face the open gulf.

This eastern shore is fringed by a salt marsh, twelve miles long and a mile or two in width, that Robert Allen called "one of the most fascinating water environments that I have ever wet my feet in." The marsh and its network of ponds, inlets, and mud flats, is the home of small sea animals, particularly the blue crab, on which whooping cranes depend for food. This marsh, together with some similar stretches on the shores of Matagorda and St. Joseph, is the true kingdom of the cranes. Here they stake out their territories and spend most of their winter days. Behind the marsh the peninsula rises into low, rolling sandy soil, densely covered with live oak and sweet-bay brush. Groves, or "mottes," of blackjack oak provide acorns and shelter from storms for a variety of creatures. The interior is host to dozens of species of birds and mammals, but the whooping cranes as a rule visit it only when storm or drought drives them from the marsh, or to feed on acorns when they are in season.

The Blackjack Peninsula was first settled in the early 1800's. Homesteaders cleared the high ground for small farms. In time a post office, a fish factory, and a general store graced the settlement. However, its remoteness made farming marginal. After 1900, the homesteaders began to drift inland. The fish factory closed. In 1923, a San Antonio millionaire named Leroy Denman bought the entire peninsula. He used it to graze cattle and as a shooting preserve. It was thanks to Denman's protection and the isolation of the peninsula that the cranes survived there, but one other aspect of Denman's ownership was less fortunate for them. When he sold to the government he retained mineral rights which provide that there may be oil exploration and drilling anywhere on the refuge. The arrangement included a royalty to the government that will eventually refund the entire purchase price of the land. This bargain was a

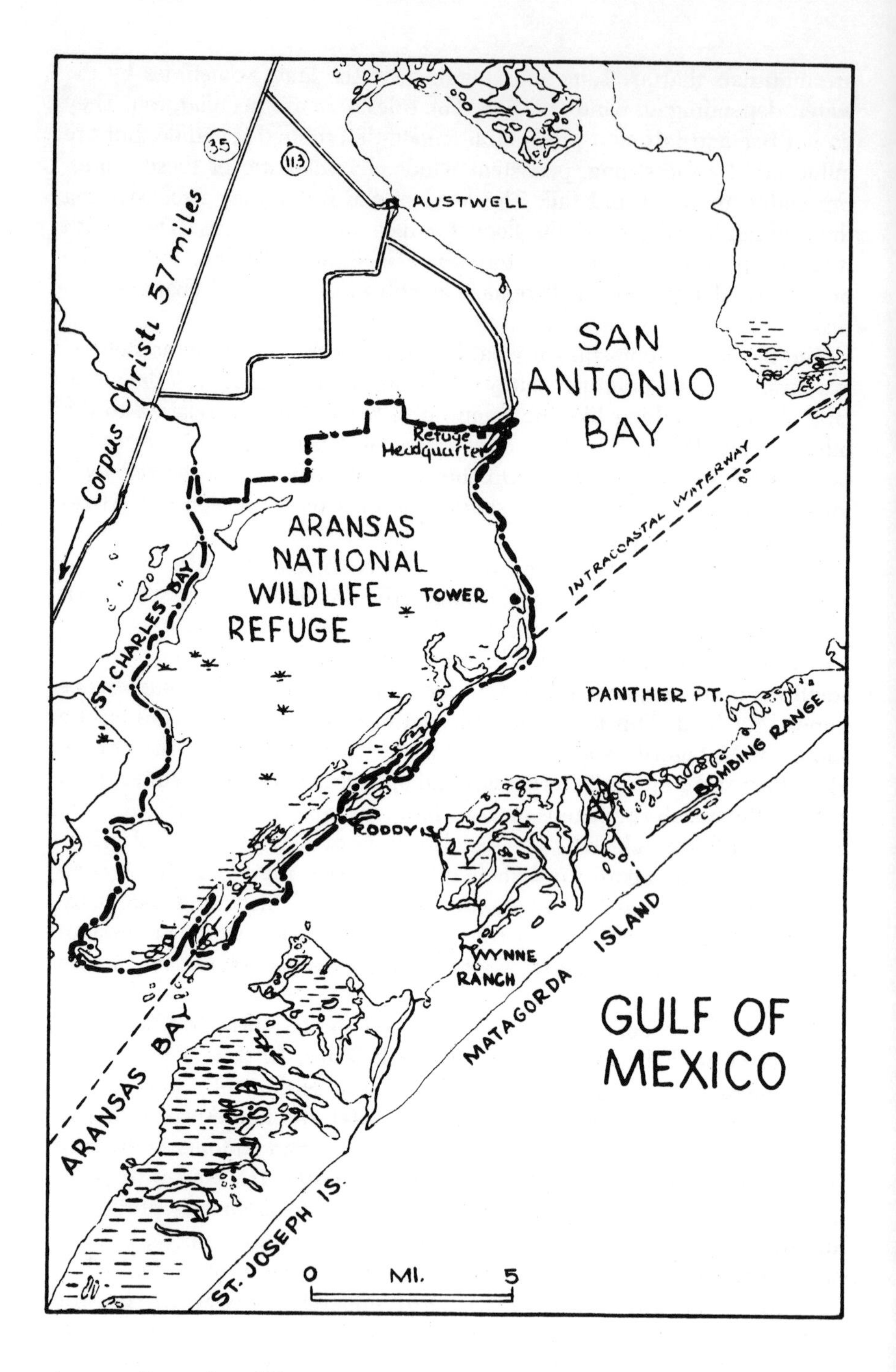

Aransas National Wildlife Refuge and Environs

good one, perhaps, for the taxpayers, but it rendered the sanctuary less than inviolable at its very inception.

In 1938, Aransas Refuge began to function with the installation of a resident manager, James O. Stevenson. His first important contribution to the cranes was an attempt to count them. Nowadays Fish and Wildlife men count the cranes from a low-flying airplane or from roads that overlook the salt flats, but in Stevenson's day the plane was not available and the roads had not been built. By tramping over the flats, Stevenson found fourteen cranes in the autumn of 1938. Four of them were rusty-colored young. Stevenson felt that, because of the difficulty of scanning the entire shoreline, he probably missed a few cranes and that there may have been as many as eighteen whooping cranes in the area.

Meanwhile, in Louisiana, John Lynch, a Fish and Wildlife Service staff biologist who had been keeping track of the small resident population of whooping cranes in the marsh at White Lake found that they had increased to thirteen.

These two reports, adding up to no more than thirty-one whooping cranes, suddenly made clear the impossibility of the Nebraska reports of large flocks. The bad news, no longer conjecture, began to seep through ornithological circles.

The first winter on the refuge was comparatively tranquil. The weather was clear and mild. Hunters shot 7,806 ducks and 136 geese in the waters around the refuge, but fortunately shot no whooping cranes. A CCC camp was built on the refuge, and the boys began to work on roads, paved with oyster shells, and on a headquarters building.

Stevenson, fascinated with the cranes, made an effort to study their behavior, noting particularly the tendency of each pair to choose a certain territory and to remain within its limits, driving off any other whoopers that sought to intrude. Then, in the weeks between mid-April and mid-May, Stevenson found fewer cranes each time he counted them, and presumed that the missing individuals had flown north. No one could do more than hope they would return.

Stevenson's summer, though isolated, could hardly have been lonely. The bureau had given a permit to the San Antonio Loan and Trust Company, representing Denman, allowing it to graze four thousand head of cattle for a fee of thirty cents per head per month. This meant that cowboys handling the cattle came and went. In addition the first explorations for oil had shown a promising area at the inland edge of the refuge, and Continental Oil, which had leased the rights from San Antonio Loan and Trust, was making preparations to drill. These workers plus the CCC boys formed a large and busy human population.

In October the first crane reappeared—then a family—followed by others, until by mid-November Stevenson counted what proved to be that year's maximum of twenty-two cranes. Six were young. One pair had brought twins.

The mild, dry winter weather of 1939–1940 gradually became drought. The cranes visited an artesian well to drink twice a day. Stevenson built a blind nearby from which he watched the cranes. In this neutral territory the crane families called a truce and did not dispute each other's right to the water. Geese, widgeons, and pintails lined up at the side and humbly waited their turn to drink when the lordly cranes had finished. One large crane disciplined any geese that got out of line.

In 1938, a strip of water around the refuge had been declared legally closed to hunting by presidential proclamation, but the ban was not immediately enforced. When, in the winter of 1939–1940, Stevenson closed these waters, it was a sorrow and annoyance to the St. Charles Bay Club, a hunting club on the shore of St. Charles Bay, whose manager was found in "closed" waters attempting to drive ducks out of the safety zone and in front of the gunners' blinds. Of the club's fifty-one blinds, thirty-three were just offshore from the refuge. Eventually the sportsmen became reconciled to the idea that the refuge actually enhanced their shooting, but at the time, Stevenson reported, they were "provoked, to say the least."

In January, Stevenson recorded the odd behavior of a family of three whooping cranes that suddenly took to frequenting inland farmlands to the southeast of the refuge. There they were perfectly visible from the highway, but paid little attention to the automobiles passing a few hundred yards from them. Stevenson was greatly relieved when, at length, they returned safely home.

The truce between man and whooping crane at Aransas was doomed to be shattered by the Army Engineers who appeared on the scene in the spring of 1940. The engineers had been inexorably working their way down the coast, dredging a channel along the shore in order to extend the Gulf Intracoastal Waterway south to Corpus Christi. Upon reaching the refuge they did not turn aside. As they surveyed the area they found that a route along the edge of the cranes' precious salt marshes would offer more protection to boats and be cheaper to maintain than the otherwise equally feasible offshore route winding through the chain of bays that bound the refuge. As the engineers pressed on through the refuge, they drained and thus destroyed acres of whooping-crane territory on the salt flats. The spoil from their ditchdigging smothered another wide area, rendering it useless as far as cranes were concerned. The loss of territory, although unfortunate, was minor compared to the main misfortune that had now befallen the cranes. Their sanctuary was now pierced by a broad highway of water, open to all comers. As Robert Allen wrote bitterly, "The ditch, nine feet deep and one hundred wide, over a three-hundred-foot right-of-way bisected the very edge of salt flats where whooping cranes had found safety for perhaps two million years. This once isolated tip is no longer secure, or isolated."

Even if the Fish and Wildlife Service had fully foreseen the sad results—the danger from guns, from disturbance, and pollution that were the inevitable results of having the Waterway on the doorstep of the refuge—there was very little they could have done about it. This was by no means the first, and far from the last, time that the plans of the engineers have collided with the interests of wildlife. Almost invariably the engineers roll on, no matter what the protests. As one official of the service, a veteran of a thousand lost battles, has sadly remarked: "To say that the Engineers are unmoved by our wishes is putting it mildly." And so, as the engineers swept through Aransas, the service could only watch sadly and philosophically, and hope for the best. It is quite likely, too, that at that time very few people thought the whooping cranes would be around long enough for conditions at Aransas to make much difference.

While the engineers were digging, the Continental Oil Company had begun drilling. On January 27, 1940, its first well blew in and caught fire. Stevenson, who was having trouble enough policing the roughnecks working the rig, now had to cope with streams of sightseers come to view the blaze. Fortunately, the well was on the inland side of the refuge, at a place called Little Devil Bayou, far from the cranes' usual haunts and in an area of low value to wildlife. The well was eventually capped, and Con Oil went to work on a second.

During April and May the twenty-two whooping cranes flew off to the peace and quiet of Canada, leaving Stevenson to a hot, busy summer.

Humble Oil began drilling in the bay just outside the water boundary of the refuge. A dredge started digging a channel in the oyster reefs. Finally news was received that the Army Air Corps proposed to use part of Matagorda Island as a bombing and machine-gun target range.

In Louisiana another misfortune was waiting in the wings. In August, 1940, a cloudburst and windstorm hit White Lake. The thirteen resident whooping cranes that John Lynch had counted the year before were flushed out of their seclusion and blown inland. From this visit to the haunts of man only six returned to the marsh. Of the seven that were lost, it is presumed that six were shot and eaten and that the seventh, though wounded by a gunshot, survived.

Any population, animal or human, has a numerical threshold below which it cannot produce enough young to counterbalance normal attrition. Apparently the six survivors at White Lake were below that threshold. By 1942 they had dwindled to five; in 1943 there were four;

the next year three. For the next two years a lonely pair hung on, but did not nest, and then, in 1947, there was only a single bird.

A year after the disastrous storm at White Lake, a fateful sequel took place. On November 25, 1941, a whooping crane with a crippled wing was brought to the Audubon Park Zoo in New Orleans. This was undoubtedly the only survivor of the seven lost White Lake cranes. The bird had been captured by a farmer in Evangeline Parish in the fall of 1940. He gave it to a Mr. La Haye of Eunice, Louisiana, who nursed it to health. La Haye assumed that his crippled pet was of no particular distinction, but a year later a Federal Game Management agent, Houston C. Gascon, happened to see the bird, and identified it as a whooping crane. The bird was brought to the zoo by Gascon and State Wildlife and Fisheries Officer John McCloskey.

The bird was received by George Douglass, who had recently become director of the Park Department and hence of the zoo. Its arrival at Audubon Park is noted on a tattered card in a filing cabinet in the zoo's office. The card reads, "Josephine . . . whooping crane . . . 4 feet tall . . . wing spread approximately seven feet . . . adult . . . pure white . . . . found in a rice field in Eunice, La., 1941 . . . donated by L. O. La Haye of Eunice, La." Handwritten in pencil across the bottom of the card are the words "because so rare priceless."

For once the concept "priceless" was almost literally true. Possession of this bird would eventually give control of the entire captive breeding population of whooping cranes to the Audubon Park Zoo. However, it is safe to assume that at the time this thought occurred to no one, including Douglass. He put the bird in a small cage, placed her on exhibit, and there she remained, causing little remark of any kind, for the next ten years.

At Aransas on October 22, 1940, Stevenson saw the first crane returned from the north, and by December he had counted twenty-six birds. There were five young. In all, the increase these first three summers seemed extremely promising.

In the spring, however, an apparently healthy group of three, a pair with their yearling, failed to migrate. They spent the summer on the refuge, but did not nest. From time to time since then, others have done the same. No one knows why.

One day in May, 1941, when all the cranes except these three had left, a string of barges tending a wildcat well, recently drilled in the bay a short distance from the east end of the refuge, suddenly discharged a quantity of oil into the water. As it happened Stevenson was standing with a visitor looking over the marshes. The visitor was Robert Allen, who had recently come to Texas on an assignment from the National

Audubon Society to study the roseate spoonbills that are found on the outer islands. The two men saw with dismay that a wide slick was slowly traveling inland toward the entrance to the canal. If the oil entered the waterway, it would wash into the ponds and mud flats, bringing an abrupt black death to the plant and animal life of the shore. There was nothing Allen and Stevenson could do, so they just watched. Then, the wind changed and the deadly stuff moved off in another direction. If the wind had not shifted when it did, the cranes would have returned to a lifeless shore, which would, quite likely, have ended their story right there.

Stevenson and Allen drove to Houston and called on the president of the oil company concerned. He listened sympathetically as they described what had almost happened. Then he said that such things occur despite the best of precautions. He turned up the palms of his hands. "Let us trust, gentlemen," he said, "that this does not happen again."

In the autumn of 1941 the whooping cranes returned, but though Stevenson searched repeatedly he was unable to locate more than fifteen birds. Of these, three had summered on the refuge; two were young of the year. Thus, of the twenty-three migrants of the previous spring, only ten had returned. "We can only wonder about the rest," Stevenson wrote as he recorded the loss of the thirteen birds in his regular report to Washington of events at Aransas. However, it is likely that not many people gave the matter much thought. At this moment Pearl Harbor tended to eclipse whooping-crane affairs no matter how unfortunate they might be.

The war began to be felt at Aransas when army and navy planes started to fly low over the refuge. Local hunting guides grumbled that revenues fell because these flights broke up the concentrations of ducks and geese. Stevenson called on military commanders at nearby bases and informed them that low-flying airplanes might drive the whooping cranes from the refuge. They promised cooperation, and in fact fewer planes flew low. The CCC camp closed, and the boys went off to war. Stevenson caught a hunter on the refuge, and charges were brought against him.

That year (1942), by enormous good fortune, the fifteen surviving cranes made their summer journey without the loss of a single adult bird, and brought back four young ones.

In July, 1943, when the nineteen cranes had left for the summer, the Army Air Force began to use its practice range on Matagorda Island. The range is a strip twenty-two miles long and three miles wide, situated ten miles southeast of the refuge headquarters, but at one point only five miles from crane territory on False Live Oak Point. The site for the range had been chosen, according to the air force, "because it would affect comparatively few people." In the years since then the range has been used for bombing practice, at both low and high altitudes, sometimes with live ammunition and sometimes only for dry runs in which an imaginary impact point is calculated by radar.

As in the case of the Army Engineers, the wishes of the Fish and Wildlife Service make no perceptible dent on the air force. However, whereas the engineers dig and move on, the air force settles down to stay. In this situation the Fish and Wildlife Service has no choice but to establish neighborly relations in an attempt to minimize the damage. This they proceeded to do at Aransas. Communications between the two services are cordial. The only trouble is that the air-force bombing range is there at all.

Despite the air activity on Matagorda, the cranes continued to use the marsh at the easterly portion of the island. This half of the island is privately owned. It is the property of a prominent Texas rancher named Toddie Lee Wynne. From time to time bombing miscalculations have resulted in the disappearance of one or two of Mr. Wynne's herd, but as far as is known no whooping cranes have been pulverized. Close calls—and there must have been some—are not on record.

5

In 1943, Stevenson wrote an article about the whooping cranes that was published in *Audubon Magazine*. Even as late as this, no one knew with certainty that the cranes at Aransas were the only migratory whooping cranes in existence. Stevenson harbored the hope that others—perhaps the birds reported as migrating through Nebraska—would still turn up, and spoke of the species as being reduced to a "sorry remnant of perhaps two hundred birds."

What was perfectly clear, however, was that new dangers had appeared at Aransas at almost the same moment that the establishment of the refuge had promised safety to the whoopers. Stevenson listed these obvious threats: bombing and machine-gun ranges established by the Army Air Corps on the barrier islands; target-shooting boatmen riding through the refuge on the Intracoastal Waterway; exploration for oil on the refuge; the drilling of oil wells in the waters of the bay. "Are the birds to be driven from their last stronghold?" he asked.

Shortly thereafter, in the autumn of 1943, sixteen of the nineteen cranes that had migrated came back to Aransas, bringing with them five young for a net gain to the flock of two birds. The twenty-one whoopers were greeted by a new manager at the refuge. Stevenson had been transferred in accordance with a Fish and Wildlife policy of moving its men from post to post at regular intervals. The new manager was Earl W. Craven. "The whoopers are still struggling for existence," Craven reported to Washington, "and there is still hope for them as long as they continue to produce young." Craven also reported that Continental Oil Company was still drilling and now had four producing wells. The skies over the refuge were still busy with airplane traffic. Craven noted that most of the wildlife on the refuge was becoming adjusted to airplanes, although the geese remained a bit nervous about them.

The twenty-one whooping cranes migrated normally in the spring of 1944 and vanished toward the north in their customary manner. On October 20, 1944, Craven saw the first autumn arrivals. A family of three alighted on the territory opposite Rattlesnake Point. By November, Craven had counted a total of eighteen whooping cranes, of which three were young. Thereafter, all during the winter, the birds behaved restlessly and moved in and out of the refuge, making it impossible to be sure of the true number. Robert Allen later guessed that four birds were overlooked or possibly had wintered off the refuge, so that the flock actually numbered twenty-two, in the winter of 1944–1945.

In an effort to locate the cranes, Craven was now making his surveys from a plane leased from a local airport. In the spring he told Washington that the whooping cranes had apparently scattered up and down the coast. They had been reported both north and south of the refuge, and often only half the flock could be found at any one time. Craven guessed that low water levels on the salt marshes had made food conditions unfavorable and caused the birds to look elsewhere for feeding grounds. In the spring of 1945 the entire flock departed for the North. It was lucky that no whoopers remained behind, for in August the refuge was in the path of a particularly savage hurricane that would surely have swept them away.

During the five years following the establishment of the Aransas Refuge, the indisputable and bleak figures on whooping cranes resulting from each winter's census in Texas were at last attracting the attention of the ornithological world. Reports published by the American Ornithologists' Union and the Wilson Club pronounced the whoopers' situation more precarious than ever and, in 1944, called for action to save the remnant of the species.

Shortly thereafter the National Audubon Society took up the problem of the cranes with the United States Fish and Wildlife Service—the new agency in the Department of the Interior that had taken over wildlife management from the Biological Survey. The director of the service was Dr. Ira N. Gabrielson. Both he and Dr. Clarence Cottam, its chief of research, were well aware that despite protection at Aransas the whoopers were holding on to life by the slenderest of threads; but, lacking funds for such obscure and exotic projects as the salvation of whooping cranes, the service was unable to take any special measures on their behalf. In this situation the National Audubon Society was the only agency in the country willing and able to lend a hand.

The National Audubon Society was formed in 1905 to meet a specific and urgent threat. The combined onslaught of sportsmen and commercial exploiters had finished off the pigeons and the parakeets; plume hunters were reducing the great egret colonies from tens of thousands of birds to a handful, and so on through a sorry list. In the case of the pigeon and the parakeet, the society came on the scene too late. It saved the egret, dramatically, by forcing the passage of laws that banned further slaughter. A generation later, however, it was apparent that human expansion posed a new and more subtle danger as it altered environment and shattered the delicate balance of plant and animal life. It is of little use to ban hunting when an entire habitat may be wiped out, as has happened in the case of the ivory-billed woodpecker, which depended on a certain kind of forest and could adapt to no other. By the 1930's the society had realized that henceforward in order to help a threatened species it would be necessary to understand how its life cycle was related to its environment and to the new conditions confronting it.

In these days when it seems that almost any conceivable subject is under scrutiny by someone, it is surprising to find that there is a wide gap in research on wildlife. Applied research, that is, studies whose results are to be used in the "management" of a species, are usually paid for either by government grants or by grants from manufacturers of arms and ammunition. In general this means that to merit study a species must be deemed either useful or pernicious. To the arms industry "useful" means desirable to hunt. Thus, while game species have been intensely investigated, the creatures that are neither pests nor playthings remain on the fringes. So-called "pure research" is not much more helpful. Its investigations may be devoted to such fascinating questions as an analysis of the lovesong of the bluebird, but in such a case its chief interest is the song rather than the bird. The results shed no light on why there are fewer bluebirds to sing. Perhaps someday a farseeing industrialist will launch a sales promotion in which a built-in bluebird is promised with every new suburban home, thus making bluebirds a useful part of our economy, as worthy of study as the corn borer and the mallard duck. Meanwhile, no one but the National Audubon Society is willing to spend significant sums on such purely quixotic projects as the perpetuation of bluebirds or, in the present case, whooping cranes.

In 1945, the president of the society was a tall, serious-minded Bostonian named John Hopkinson Baker. He was the son of George Pierce Baker, director of the famous drama workshop at Harvard and, later, Yale. He had been an amateur naturalist since boyhood, a World War I pilot, and a successful businessman before he took on, at the age of fifty, the leadership of the society. One of the first questions to cross his desk was that of the whooping cranes, and it was his decision that the society should intervene.

As John Baker surveyed the situation of the cranes, it was obvious that there was an almost complete lack of information on which to base a program of help. Not only did no one know, surely, how many whooping cranes there were; but there were no reliable data on the most elementary factors in their life cycle. Their food, nesting habits, the rearing of their young, their behavior on the long flight to their mysterious nesting grounds, all presented unanswered questions. During the thirties the society had come to the aid of the ivory-billed woodpecker, the California condor, and the roseate spoonbill by underwriting exhaustive biological studies. It now decided to do the same for the whooping cranes. John Baker conferred with Gabrielson and Cottam of the Fish and Wildlife Service. An alliance called the "Cooperative Whooping Crane Project" was formed. Its announced purpose was to determine "what steps may reasonably be taken toward further protection and restoration of the species." Beyond this the terms of the partnership were unwritten, an omission that the society may later have viewed with regret.

The first step in the project was, of course, to find a biologist willing to take on what promised to be a long, strenuous, and financially thankless task. The job would involve not only a study of the whooping cranes at Aransas but also a search for the hidden nests whose location was considered one of the most crucial questions in the puzzle of how to preserve the species. At that moment, in early 1945, the society's research director, Robert Porter Allen, who had studied the spoonbills and was obviously the man for the whooping-crane job, was in the army. Most of the other men who might have qualified were unavailable for the same reason. The gap was filled, momentarily, when a Canadian devotee of the whooping crane, Fred Bard, curator of the Provincial Museum in Regina, Saskatchewan, offered to search for the whoopers' nests. In the summer of 1945 Bard spent two months in fruitless airplane flights over central Saskatchewan, without seeing so much as the tail feather of a whooping crane.

That autumn the Whooping Crane Project was taken on by an ornithologist, Dr. Olin Sewall Pettingill, Jr., who spent several winter months studying the birds at Aransas. In the summer of 1946, Mr. Terris Moore, president of the New England Museum of Natural History, offered the use of a plane and his own services as pilot. Pettingill and Moore flew over several thousand miles of what seemed promising territory in Alberta and Saskatchewan in an unavailing search for whooping-crane nests. In the autumn Pettingill had to drop the project in favor of a teaching job, but by then, luckily, Robert Allen was on his way home.

Bob Allen, then forty-one years old, was a stocky, dark-haired man with a strong-featured, smiling look of humor and friendliness that belied both the sophistication of his mind and the fierceness of his dedication to his cause: the protection of threatened species. His character combined a capacity for strong feeling with a rare sensitivity and gentleness. What made these qualities so effective was an extraordinarily patient doggedness—once committed, it seemed impossible for him to give up until the cause was won. At the time Allen took on the whooping-crane project, no one could foresee what the job would entail. When he had finished his monograph, he had spent three years and three months of intensive study, twenty-seven of them in fieldwork. He traveled more than twenty thousand miles by plane and six thousand by jeep, searching

Robert Allen, photographed in a boat at the time he was studying the whooping cranes.

the Canadian wilderness for the secret nesting sites. He spent many freezing nights in tents; some of them in northwest Saskatchewan where late spring sleet storms suddenly iced the canvas, and others on the flats of Aransas where chill, hard "northers" can blow exhaustingly night and day. He often ate badly and overworked for long stretches of time. These are conditions that can appear romantic from a comfortable distance, but are more likely to be depressing when experienced at first hand. In Allen's case his sense of the romance of the whooping cranes proved unquenchable, no matter what the conditions of his work.

Allen wrote a great deal about the birds: a number of articles, a popular book, and the monograph with its supplement on the nesting grounds. In all these, even in his most objective scientific reports, he conveyed the sense that he had fallen in love with the cranes and become committed to their cause. He presented the case for the survival of the cranes not simply as the continuance or extinction of one species among many now in danger, but as the cause of all simple, beautiful, and defenseless living things vanishing before the relentless force of human expansion. Since Allen was a romantic, somewhat of a mystic, and a man of violent belief and fierce determination, he refused to concede that the outcome of the conflict is inevitable.

Robert Allen was born in South Williamsport, Pennsylvania, on April 24, 1905. His early surroundings were a combination of the literate and the rural. His mother was a schoolteacher and his father a lawyer. Their home was in mountain country where deer, bear, bobcat, and other game survived in abundance. Allen's own account of his boyhood makes it clear that he was called to his work with wildlife as surely as some receive the summons to the Church. In Allen's case the first mystic whisper came when, at the age of ten, he read Ernest Thompson Seton's *Two Little Savages.* For a while thereafter Allen spent as much time as possible in the role of an Indian stealing through ancestral hunting grounds. Seton has endowed the wild with magic for many young boys; for Allen this magic remained constant to the end of his life.

By the time he reached high school, Allen had joined a junior Audubon Club and shifted from deerslayer to bird watcher. Thenceforward ornithology was the only thing he really cared about. Upon graduation he reluctantly left the woods to enter Lafayette College in Easton, Pennsylvania. He spent two years there; in his opinion, quite uselessly. Allen described himself at this period: "In my outmoded Norfolk jacket I was a trifle rural among my new friends, although I knew that I could outrun the whole lot of them on a mountain trail, outpaddle them in a canoe, and make jackasses of them in a river-bottom swamp. I did learn a few things about the world that lay beyond Bald Eagle Mountain, but I remained an undisciplined nonconformist, incapable of learning many of the graces and determined to find a way of life wherein the kind of shoes you wore and the sort of knot in your tie were of no importance."

As a practical matter Allen found that his skill in ornithology seemed unlikely to finance any way of life whatever. For a time he avoided the question of a career by taking a job on a freighter bound for Singapore. In three years he sailed twice around the world. His adventures included a shipwreck in the Sulu Sea. He came home forty-eight cents richer.

Ashore in New York, Allen went to a party at which he met a girl named Evelyn Sedgwick who had just graduated from the Juilliard School of Music, and fell in love with her. Love produced a sudden urge for solvency, and Allen set out to look for work. He called on Dr. Chapman, of the American Museum of Natural History, with whom he had once corresponded on the subject of birds. Chapman sent him to see Dr. T. Gilbert Pearson, then president of the National Audubon Society, who gave Allen a trial job sorting books in the basement. Allen was jubilant. He had found a milieu in which the knot in his tie was not important; he was dealing with books and birds, and he was able to marry Miss Sedgwick.

In 1930, when Allen came to the National Audubon Society, it was modestly housed over a funeral parlor on Broadway. During the next ten years the society not only expanded but, in accordance with new needs, began a program of research and field studies. Allen was promoted from book sorter to full-time ornithologist. He emerged from the basement to make a study of gulls on the Maine coast. A friend commented that sending Allen into the field was like "ordering a duck back to water." The society had also begun to set up a department of sanctuaries. In 1934, after growing a moustache in order to look old enough to satisfy the board of directors, Allen became sanctuary director. Five years later, in 1939, the plight of the roseate spoonbill, a large, gaudily beautiful, shore-dwelling bird native to Florida and Texas, became urgent. Allen was assigned to a full-scale study. With his family, which by then included a son and daughter, he moved to Tavernier, a little town on Key Largo at the tip of Florida. The Allens set up housekeeping in a trailer close to the home of the spoonbills on Bottlepoint Key. A year later he was able to make recommendations that undoubtedly saved that colony of birds. His spoonbill monograph, published in 1942, is considered a classic life history. By the time it had appeared in print, Allen was in the army, on sea duty, serving as a mate on an army minelayer.

When, on his return, John Baker told Allen that the whooping cranes were now his problem, he already had an inkling of what the project would entail. Six years before, the study of spoonbills had taken him to the Texas coast, where he saw his first whooping crane. "I wondered idly," he later wrote, "what poor, unsuspecting soul would some day be assigned the rugged task of making a full-scale study of them."

Meanwhile, at Aransas, the whoopers had been doing slightly better than holding their own. In the winter of 1945 official refuge figures showed only seventeen cranes, but Dr. Pettingill, who twice searched the coast by plane, concluded that the total population was twenty-five, with nine of the cranes spending most of their time on the island of Matagorda. There were, however, only three young whoopers, including a pair of twins.

In the spring of 1946 four of the flock stayed behind to summer on the refuge. Two were the young twins who, for some unexplained reason, failed to follow their parents north. The others were two single birds, both of them crippled and unable to fly, who joined forces during the summer. Luckily the summer weather was calm and the four came through without incident. When, in the autumn of 1946, the rest of the flock returned, they had again brought with them only three youngsters. Robert Allen reached Aransas in November to begin work on the Whooping Crane Project, and found that the world's population of migratory whooping cranes was twenty-five.

6

When Allen came to the Aransas Refuge in November, 1946, it was approached as it is now, by a state road that cuts through vast flat, tilled fields. In winter the furrows look like black corduroy stretched out to the horizon. Far-off houses and a few windmills stand up like ships at sea. In this openness the sky seems higher and wider than elsewhere. Often the sky is busy with fast-moving clouds that darken and lighten the landscape in quick succession. There may be sudden showers followed by dramatically golden sunbursts. Gradually, approaching the shore of San Antonio Bay, the land becomes more wooded, with clumps of oak and mesquite breaking the geometric pattern of the fields. Just before the gates of the refuge there is a pebbly shore, white with shells—at the moment inhabited only by a collection of rusted tin shacks called Pete's Camp—and beyond it the shallow waters of the bay whose horizon is dotted by offshore oil rigs and the lumpy craft that tend them.

The road leads through modest gates to the refuge, and to a different landscape. Here there has been little cutting for over thirty years. There are handsome groves of oaks and everywhere lush tangles of shrub and vine. Things are more manicured now than they were when Allen arrived. There are a neat, cement-block headquarters building and pleasant little houses for the staff. At almost any time there are apt to be white-tailed deer—two or three or perhaps more—browsing in the clearing around the buildings. When visitors arrive, the deer stare as though incredulous at the intrusion, and after a moment's thought leap suddenly into the thickets with a rocking motion, as though their legs were pogo sticks.

Although Aransas is tidier now than it was when Allen worked there, its essential appearance is unchanged. The shell-paved roads wind past shrub and thicket and grove. Armadillos creep nearsightedly through the wiry grass. It is possible to glimpse wary, tough little javelinas—small, native peccary—and big wild pigs that are descended from European boars released there years ago by Leroy Denman. From time to time there is a boar roundup followed by roast pork on the menus of deserving local institutions and a barbecue for the staff. There are thirty or forty species of mammals on the refuge—and almost three hundred species of birds have been sighted there. But all this goes on in the wooded uplands, and is for the most part remote from the world of the whooping cranes out on the marsh.

In November, the Allens arrived and set up housekeeping in the town of Austwell, eight miles from the gates of Aransas. Austwell was, and still is, an extremely modest settlement (present population 287) housed in a collection of gray frame buildings. The post office is in the rear of the general store, but the social headquarters in Allen's day was in Cap Daniel's combination beer parlor, gas station and garage. Here Allen sounded local opinion and found that the town's leading citizens were either indifferent to whooping cranes or resentful because birds that had been declared legally inedible were supported in idleness on taxpayers' money. Allen regarded it as an important victory when, two years later, the proprietor, a great collector of junk and mementos, not only asked for a photograph of a whooping crane but, in order to make room for it, unhesitatingly wrenched from the wall a large lithograph of Judge Roy Bean holding court west of the Pecos. In Texas this is almost a sacred scene. Such a gratifying change in local attitude was due to a great deal of patient missionary work on the part of both the Allens. Mrs. Allen, a woman with a talent for making friends in whatever social milieu she finds herself, did not scorn to put her Juilliard training to work. She played the organ in Austwell's tiny church, and little by little helped to convince even the most skeptical of her neighbors that ornithologists are not necessarily lunatic feather collectors.

On a dismally gray, cold day in November, Allen began his study of the cranes. He and the new refuge manager, Bud Keefer, who had recently replaced Craven, tramped along the higher ground overlooking the flats until they caught sight of two white forms, distinct against the golden-tan sand. Allen made his first field notes on the cranes: "Two adult wh. cranes on wet mud flat in Redfish Slough. Fed a little and rested, preening. ½ to ¾ mi. distant from our position on dyke." Later he added: "I remember that those first two birds seemed very far away—not only in a physical sense. Their arrogant bearing, the trim of their sails, as it were, would intimidate the most brash investigator. I reached our cabin that first night feeling very humble and not too happy."

Getting close to the whooping cranes in a physical sense was a very real problem. The birds proved to be extremely wary of anyone moving on foot. Later, Allen found that they are less easily disturbed by the approach of an automobile and that a boat on the Intracoastal Waterway can come within fifty yards as long as it keeps moving at a steady pace. But Allen had no boat and there was no automobile road from which

A border skirmish photographed at Aransas. The pair at left is driving an intruding family from its territory.

he could scan the marsh. For his first surveys he and Keefer used a tractor to draw an old farm wagon—Keefer at the controls and Allen standing in the wagon, trying to hang on to his field glasses and the wagon at the same time—following a rough trail along the twelve miles of shorefront.

In these first winter months crane-watching remained frustrating, chilly work. For a time it seemed as though a half a mile were as close as Allen would get to them. Then one day he suddenly surprised a pair not fifty yards away. "They were already moving," he later wrote, "sounding their bugle-clear trumpet blast of warning and running with amazingly lengthy strides before getting airborne. The red skin on top

Flight takeoff and landing.

of their heads stood out clearly, and so did the grim, almost fierce cast of their features . . . like great, satin-white bombers, with their immense wings flicking upward in short arcs and their heavy bodies fighting for altitude, still calling, they glided over the tops of the scrub, slowly gaining elevation. . . . I had forgotten how cold I was . . . my hand was shaking when I started to write my notes."

At one point in his efforts to get close to the cranes, Allen, who had noticed that the birds were indifferent to cattle wandering on their territory, went so far as to construct a portable blind in the shape of a bull. His contraption, consisting of a red canvas hide stretched over a wire frame, turned out so convincing that he named it "Bovus absurdus." This realism was almost Allen's undoing. He had placed Bovus on the marsh and hidden himself inside, waiting for cranes to appear, when, to his horror, he saw a real bull—huge and baleful—advancing to challenge the supposed interloper. For a few dreadful moments the real bull glared at Bovus, and its quaking occupant, with puzzled hostility. Then, apparently deeming Bovus unworthy of combat, the bull wandered off. Allen scrambled out of his disguise determined to find other means of observing cranes.

As Allen became more familiar with the marshes, he found vantage points from which he could creep within fifty yards of feeding cranes without flushing the birds. Gradually each family took on an identity in his mind. He named them according to the territory they occupied—the Slough Pair, Middle Pond Family, Dike Pair, and so on. Gradually, too, he became acquainted with the invisible boundaries separating the domains of each pair, and began to discover some of the essential rules of whooping-crane behavior.

In addition to watching the cranes as they went about their daily rounds, Allen spent long hours painstakingly putting together notes about the habitat on which they depended. He studied the action of wind and tide on the food supply in the ponds, and how this in turn caused the cranes to move here or there. He counted two hundred marine worms per cubic foot of Aransas mud, and watched the comings and goings of the blue crab, a vital link in the food chain that feeds the cranes.

When Robert Allen took over the Whooping Crane Project from Dr. Pettingill, he noted with interest that Pettingill had discovered two whooping cranes in captivity: Josephine, the White Lake survivor who had been at the New Orleans Zoo since 1941, and the one-eyed whooping crane, now named Pete, who had been kept by the Gothenburg Gun Club in Nebraska since 1936. Although no one knew the sex of these birds, Pettingill had suggested that bringing them together might be worth a try. Allen was intrigued by the idea, and decided to take time off from the work at Aransas to visit New Orleans and look at Josephine. He recorded his impressions in these notes:

"Audubon Park, New Orleans, December 4, 1946. I found the second known whooping crane in captivity in an ordinary exhibition pen, between similar pens containing a lone sarus crane on one side and a group of peafowl on the other. The sign on the wire of the cage, black letters painted on a white board: 'whooping crane—North America.' Most people visiting this section of the zoo were more attracted by the Nile Hippos. Whether this bird is a male or a female is impossible to decide. It is evidently in good or even excellent health, alert and with a good appetite. According to the employees of the zoo it will eat almost anything offered to it; peanuts, popcorn, potato chips, bits of bread and uneaten portions of hamburger, frankfurters. . . . We tried salted peanuts and the crane came close to the wire, catching them in the air as they were thrown through the netting. As it approached and while waiting for additional offerings it gave a low clucking note. Every now and then, as a number of salted peanuts were eaten, the whooper walked with dignity to its concrete water trough and drank, raising its head to swallow. The tameness of the bird is remarkable in view of its shyness in nature. It seems perfectly adapted to its life behind wire, and seems on good terms with its environment; with the crowds of staring people, the noisy children, the traffic along the adjoining road, the shrill blast of the nearby train whistle and even the endless barking of a seal in an adjacent aquarium.

"This captive whooper is an appealing individual, and even though its confinement has taken from it some of its majesty, its very tameness lends it a charm that is undeniable. And yet much of the majesty remains, even in the act of catching peanuts in midair. . . ."

As it happened, the zoo director, George Douglass, was not in his office that day, and he and Allen did not meet.

During the winter Allen made one other excursion from Aransas. He had still not given up hope that there might be other whooping cranes besides those at the refuge. In a plane chartered by the Fish and Wildlife Service he flew low along the entire coast from Louisiana to Mexico, but saw no whoopers. At the same time the Fish and Wildlife Service sent Dr. Saunders, the ornithologist who had originally surveyed Aransas, to search the former haunts of the whooping cranes in Mexico, again to no avail. Now the ornithological world at last regretfully concluded that the twenty-five cranes wintering at Aransas and the Louisiana remnant at White Lake—by then reduced to two—were the only whooping cranes left at large in the world.

In March of 1947, Allen temporarily put aside his biological studies at Aransas to take up another phase of the work, a study of the whoopers' migration and a search for the nesting grounds. From an analysis of old reports Allen felt sure that the migrating cranes followed a more or less fixed pathway north, and he guessed that at one point they would cross the Big Bend of the Platte River in Nebraska. He left Aransas ahead of the cranes—who would not start their flight until April—hoping to intercept them in what would be one of the most unlikely rendezvous ever attempted. If he succeeded in meeting whooping cranes in Nebraska, he would know how long they had taken on this first leg of the migration, and thus calculate when they would reach the mysterious nesting grounds.

Allen chose North Platte, Nebraska, as his headquarters. The local paper obligingly printed his request that anyone sighting a whooping crane telephone him at the Hotel Pawnee. During the next month he got tips daily from housewives, truckdrivers, farmers, and other bird watchers. Collectively they reported 144 whooping cranes. Allen checked each report, and identified the birds as ring-billed gulls, white pelicans, lesser sandhills, or snow geese.

In the first week of April the cranes at Aransas began to move about restlessly, and even to join up in groups as though some attraction were breaking down the social barriers of winter. The refuge manager counted the cranes daily and wired Allen each time he found a family or group missing from its usual haunts, presumably having started on the long flight north. Two crippled cranes remained on the refuge for the summer. Allen had mapped out a two-hundred-mile stretch of the Platte River where the whooping cranes were most likely to appear, and he tried to patrol at least part of the area each day. During the two weeks that whooping cranes were in flight, he flew 800 miles, drove 3,172 miles along the river, and walked more miles of river bottom than he could keep track of.

Finally, on April 14, he got news of a trio of whooping cranes, identified by a reliable informant, near Overton, Kansas. Since the only trio in flight had left Aransas on April 9, Allen now knew that the cranes had flown 920 miles in four days and a few hours.

Allen redoubled his efforts to be everywhere along the whooper front at once, but for five days there were only false alarms. Then, at last, he made his improbable rendezvous. "My five birds landed in Earl Mathers' corn stubble field, three miles east of North Platte at 7:35 A.M. April 19," Allen wrote to Baker. "Thanks to the radio publicity, he recognized them, dropped his farm chores, and sped one mile to a telephone. Meanwhile his wife saw the whoopers move out, flying off southwest. Shortly after 8 A.M. I was at the Mathers farm. No whoopers, but a hundred and twenty-four white pelicans were on the nearby Diversion Dam. After fruitlessly trudging the adjacent river bottom with Mathers, I drove to the airport and chartered a plane. In ten minutes I located the whoopers bunched together on a sandbar in the South Platte River." As the plane swept low over the birds, Allen saw a tinge of russet in the plumage of one of them and thus recognized it as the youngster of the North Family that had left Aransas in company with their winter neighbors, the Slough Pair. Allen felt as though he were greeting old friends.

The next day the whoopers had moved on. Allen got a few more reports of cranes sighted on their way to the Canadian border. After that, their trail vanished. Ahead of them lay the most dangerous part of their journey, over the wheatlands and prairies of Saskatchewan, once the heart of their territory. Here the farmers are particularly hostile to any birds that invade their grainfields, and here, Allen suspected, the whoopers, particularly the unmated yearlings, may be tempted to linger, lured by what he called their "biotic niche."

As the cranes vanished toward the north, Allen prepared to pick up the search for the nesting grounds where Dr. Pettingill had left off the summer before. Mrs. Allen and their two children joined him and, equipped with camping gear, they set forth in a station wagon and trailer, headed for the Canadian bush.

Although to hunt for twenty-odd birds, even big white ones, in millions of acres of wilderness presented a fantastically difficult assignment, Allen was convinced that finding the nests was of crucial importance in order to answer a number of biological questions. He was vitally interested in knowing what percentage of the flock was attempting to breed and how many young were being lost because of weather, predators, or other factors on the breeding ground. A count of fledglings at the nesting ground compared with the number of young reaching Aransas would show what proportion were lost on the fall migration. Finally, of course, it seemed important that conservationists find the nesting grounds before some commercial project stumbled over and destroyed them.

As Allen set out on his search, the trail of the migrating whoopers was dim indeed. Plotted on a map, all the available clues—and there were not many—seemed to describe a straight line from Aransas to Regina, Saskatchewan, but then the birds fanned out toward the northwest, and vanished. Allen decided to drive north of Regina to the end of the road and then search by air.

Each summer the Canadian Fish and Wildlife Service sends a small plane to make an aerial census of waterfowl nesting in the Northwest Territories. The service's biologist, Bob Smith, was eager to help in the search for whooping-crane nests, and the service agreed that he should take Allen along in the plane.

In early May, Allen and his family drove to Flotten Lake, Saskatchewan, at the edge of the bush, and made camp. Allen found it a disappointingly busy wilderness. Indians, loggers, and mink ranchers had taken over all the marshes and lakes that might have sheltered nesting whooping cranes.

On June 6 Smith picked up Allen, and the two men spent weeks flying at low altitude and scanning the wilderness beneath for any sign of a white bird. Their flight path, covering almost six thousand miles, took them across northern Alberta, then north to the Lake Claire area, and finally to Great Slave Lake in the District of Mackenzie. Here, on June 25, finding nothing but endless barrens ahead, unlikely for cranes, they turned back in defeat and headed south and east toward their base at Fort Smith. Their route home took them over the northern corner of a wilderness preserve named Wood Buffalo Park. Beneath the plane was a wild region of muskeg, sparsely covered with tamarack and pitted with pothole ponds and lakes. Here Allen's psychic sense should have given him a nudge, but, as the plane suddenly ran into heavy rain that blotted out his view of the ground, Allen noted only, "1:40 P.M. Rain squall. Rough going. Poor visibility all the way in . . . This ends our search. We have no further possibilities on our list!"

Years later, when the nests had been found, Allen realized that as he wrote those words he was directly over the whooping cranes' nesting place, at that moment veiled by the sheets of rain.

If Allen's search had produced no whoopers' nests it had at least stirred a wide public interest in the quest. Most news accounts were friendly, but one Canadian magazine wrote of "a bird's nest hunt that has cost $75,000 without an egg yet to show for it." The truth was, of course, that the search had been done on a shoestring. Allen's flights with Smith were combined with the service's regular surveys, and cost the taxpayers nothing extra, but the story launched a rumor of extravagance that haunted the Whooping Crane Project for years.

More helpfully, *Life* magazine ran a story on the cranes that stirred sympathy for their plight, but also added its mite of confusion. It spoke of a plan to trail the cranes to their nesting grounds. Some readers assumed that Allen, aboard a plane, would cruise along beside the birds at 45 m.p.h., wing to wing and perhaps roosting on an adjoining sandbar at night. Helpful readers suggested that the birds be banded with "radar bands" to make such tracking easier. Somehow this caused the air force to issue a straight-faced report on "minimum reflective surface for radar waves," and the technical inadvisability of following metal-banded birds with radar-equipped aircraft.

7

On his return to Texas after the summer search of 1947, Allen again took up his study of the habitat at Aransas while he waited, in considerable suspense, for the migrant cranes to come back from Canada. He was happy to see that the two crippled whooping cranes that had remained on the refuge had come safely through the summer. He named them the "Summer Pair."

In early October an east wind that blew day after day filled the pond system of the refuge to overflowing with salt water so that a bounteous harvest of blue crabs and small marine creatures awaited the whooping cranes. On October 21 the first migrant whooping crane, a single, was seen on the refuge. Five days later it was joined by a pair and a trio of adults. The first pair to bring back a youngster arrived November 2. Allen was able to watch them as they rested and fed near Mustang Lake. They seemed very quiet, and visibly tired by their tremendous journey.

Day by day more travelers returned. Allen checked off each arrival with mounting satisfaction. A second young bird arrived, then a third. Families with young are often the last to arrive because they must fly more slowly to accommodate the youngster. Finally all twenty-three birds that had migrated in the spring were back, safe and sound, and there were six young birds with them. Counting the Summer Pair, there was now the fine total of thirty-one whooping cranes; the highest in the nine years that records had been kept at Aransas and the third time on the record that there had been no losses during the summer.

Allen now took up the problem of how to spy on the private lives of the whoopers. Considering the failure of Bovus absurdus, he abandoned the idea of a portable blind, and decided to try to attract them by scattering corn in strategic locations.

The cranes were briefly enthusiastic about these handouts. Then, to Allen's dismay, all but one family tired of corn, and would stalk off to their ponds to fish, leaving Allen alone in his blind. The exceptional family, however, saved the day for Allen. They were the Middle Pond Family, a fine pair with a young bird. Their appetite for corn remained constant. Allen worked out a method of baiting an area near the blind in the early dawn while the Family still slept in their night roost across the pond, then creeping into his hiding place to await their arrival.

Once the birds were near, he dared not even sneeze lest he give the whole show away—and sometimes he sat in his cramped hiding place watching for ten hours at a stretch. In these hours of busy, quiet vigil Allen filled notebook after notebook with the tiny details that make up the winter life of the whooping crane. Rarely has a creature been so painstakingly documented.

When whooping cranes are *en famille* it is easy, Allen found, to tell the sexes apart. The male is not only larger than the female; he is also the acknowledged head of the family. It is he who decides where to feed, when to rest, when to move on. His mate and young may wander from his side, but they always return to him, not he to them. He is not influenced by their whims. His chief occupation is to guard and defend his family, and this is a role he takes with extreme seriousness. "His head is always snapping up to attention, his cold, yellow eyes scanning the complete arc of the horizon," Allen wrote. Even his step, the way he holds his head seem to express the solemnity of his responsibility.

The attitudes of the female, on the other hand, seemed to Allen to convey a gentler, more domestic character. Although she will support her mate in defensive actions, she seems to leave decisions in these matters up to him, as though she acted upon his orders. Her main activity is the care and feeding of her young. In the early winter months she keeps the youngster always at her side, and painstakingly teaches it the primary business of life—getting food.

In the autumn as the cranes arrive—in pairs, families, or singly—there is a short period in which the birds shift about on the marsh. The wanderings of the single birds, particularly, give a sense of confusion to the territorial scene. Then, in a series of brief, but intense, ceremonial encounters the strongest pairs establish their land titles. Thereafter, except for slight misunderstandings and skirmishes at the borders, there is usually a quiet and peaceful routine throughout the winter. The social relations of the whooping cranes on the wintering ground are as cool and orderly as in the most decorous suburban community.

The occupants of a territory, Allen found, do not usually leave that territory from the time they claim it until just prior to the spring migration. Toward the end of March, as migration nears, the rigid segregation breaks down, but until then each pair or family lives strictly alone. Cranes spending the winter in a territory at the east end of the salt flats never see those in territories at the west end. The birds move inland only under special conditions: when a severe "norther" drives them to find shelter in the oak groves, or "mottes," that dot the higher land behind the marshes; when they are attracted by some special delicacy, such as a new hatch of frogs in a freshwater pond; or in a drought year when the brackish water of their feeding ponds becomes too saline and they must search for fresher drinking water elsewhere.

Allen charted fourteen territories strung like adjoining house lots along the shore of the refuge. He felt that the limits of each may have been established many whooping-crane generations in the past and that each pair returns to the same territory year after year—or attempts to—for it is always possible that a stronger pair will evict a weaker. Conceivably, territories are handed down in whooping-crane families. If so, it is likely that primogeniture would apply.

Each territory on Allen's map covers a little more than four hundred acres, and includes all the necessities of whooping-crane winter life. For the most part each is true salt flat, with waterfront for feeding, brackish ponds for drinking and sleeping, and an inland border of oak brush in which to shelter when the wind is high. Not all the territories are equally desirable. The best of all at Aransas, judging by the fact that birds that stay behind in the summer always choose it and that in winter its owners defend it with outstanding zeal, is the Middle Pond territory. Like most of the others it has about a mile of beachfront, but its superiority, Allen felt, derived from its varied and well-balanced complex of ponds and estuaries, which remain stocked with food after others have failed.

Geese and whooping cranes are among the few birds in which the family does not break up at the end of the breeding season. In each case they migrate together to the winter quarters, spend the entire winter as a family, and do not separate until some time during the spring journey north, or perhaps even later. Social status, among whooping cranes, depends upon the marital and parental situation. At the top of the social order are a pair with a young bird. It appears that the presence of the

Male of Middle Family chasing the Extra Family.

youngster stimulates a quicker temper and a fiercer attachment to home. Thus parents will defend their territory with greater determination than a childless couple, and usually triumph in a dispute. A mated pair, though childless, in turn makes stronger territorial claims than do either the lonely "singles"—who may be widowed or adolescent birds—or "companions," birds whose relationship is purely platonic. Singles or companions surrender their territory to the first challenger. They then wander, living hand to mouth as it were, chivied by the lords of whatever territories they chance to invade.

Whooping cranes are monogamous, and the attachment within a family is strong. A widowed parent continues to care for a young one. Both widows and widowers will accept new mates. However, it is suspected, on the basis of evidence that is not confined to the bird world, that the male whooping crane will make marital readjustments more readily than will the female.

No one knows at what age whooping cranes become mature and mate. Nor does anyone know when they become too old to produce fertile eggs. The oldest whooping crane on record lived to be more than forty—how much more is again unknown. This was a female purchased in 1892 by a certain Lord Lilford, who kept many species of cranes at Lilford Hall in England. For many years this bird, which lacked a mate, laid infertile eggs. When it ceased to lay eggs of its own, it brooded the eggs, also infertile, of a Manchurian crane with which it was penned. This whooper died on August 19, 1930, presumably of old age. At the time Allen wrote his monograph, the staying powers of Josephine and Crip had not yet been demonstrated, and he could find no evidence on which to base a guess concerning the whooper's life-span. In the wild, of course, there are few species whose members regularly reach old age. Most whooping cranes in recent times have died violently. Since 1938, more than a hundred yearling whooping cranes have been recorded at Aransas. Had "natural causes" been their only enemy, and these all survived to breed, the flock would now be many hundreds strong.

Documenting the behavior of the subadult whooping cranes is a difficult matter. By the time it is a year old the young whooper has lost the outward signs of immaturity and from a distance cannot be distinguished from an adult. Thus, at Aransas, Allen could not determine which of the singles were subadults and which unmated for some other reason. From an analysis of records of birds sighted during the summer, he concluded that although unmated birds migrate they do not go the full distance to the breeding grounds but become what he called "summer wanderers."

Single whooping cranes, moving about in response to varying food and water conditions, have been reported in the prairie provinces over an extremely wide area. They have turned up in central Saskatchewan and in sections of western Alberta. Often they appear close to settlements in the neighborhood of crane nesting locations abandoned many years ago. Sometimes these nonbreeders travel together, in pairs, or even small groups, but quite obviously do not nest. Allen estimated that as much as 50 percent of the flock, during the years that he observed it, were in the nonbreeding category. How many of them were young, where they went in summer, and when they mated were things that he would have given a great deal to know.

The first whooping crane Allen came to know personally, as it were, was the male of the Summer Pair, a large and lordly individual that Allen named Crip because of his damaged left wing. Although Crip was unable to fly, he was strong and alert. Once Allen and Olaf Wallmo decided to corner Crip, and learned at first hand how fast a whooping crane can walk. The two men advanced on Crip from opposite sides of the marsh. "Crip calmly hiked up his bad wing," Allen later wrote, "and, head high, started off with those steady twenty-three-inch strides that a crane uses when he wants to run down a skittering blue crab or outwalk a couple of boy scouts, which is what we felt like. Olaf and I, floundering across mudholes, were hopelessly outdistanced in ten minutes." Crip had joined forces with another flightless bird that, like him, had probably been shot on the way south, and they had spent the summer of 1947 together on the salt flats of the choice Middle Pond territory, only to be ignominiously evicted by the stronger pair with young that Allen knew as the "Middle Pond Family."

Eventually Crip and his mate settled on unclaimed territory near the canal in the vicinity of what is known as Rattlesnake Point Road. Allen put out corn for them here, as he had for the Middle Pond Family. They took to it and quickly learned to come for it daily. They seldom wandered far from the baited area except to fish along the canal near the lower end of the road.

Although the Middle Pond male had triumphed over Crip, he still had the Dike Pair to the east to keep in line. On December 19, for instance, Allen made these notes: "At 2:07 (as the Middle Ponders were preening and resting on a sandbar), the pair occupying the Dike territory to the east, called. It was the usual challenging call, repeated several times. The Middle Pond male responded at once. Drawing himself to what seemed an amazing height, bill pointing straight up, he threw an answering challenge into the air. On the second call the female joined him, the young bird, although suddenly alert, made no sound. Abruptly all three took off, the male arching his neck and beginning his take-off a fraction of a second ahead of the other two. They flew about fifty yards to the east, which brought them to the buffer strip between the two territories. Then, with another series of calls, they ran forward, launched themselves in a low, skimming flight and headed straight for the offending Dike Pair. This carried them well inside the Dike Pair's territory.

They seemed to feel that this was enough to satisfy their honor, for they landed again, nearly two hundred yards short of where the two Dike birds were standing, their heads high and whole manner one of extreme alertness. This ended the affair . . . both groups soon resumed their endless feeding, the Family gradually working back into their own bailiwick. This was a typical demonstration of the zeal and overpowering confidence of pairs with young, compared to a pair without young."

Allen had the opportunity to watch an unusual territorial problem when, in December, 1948, a lone adult accompanied by one youngster made a belated arrival. From the parent bird's manner Allen guessed it to be a female. Apparently she had lost her mate along the migration route. From her late arrival it seemed likely that the male had been badly wounded, but lingered long enough to keep his family at his side for some weeks. When the two arrived, all the choice refuge territories were already occupied.

"This 'Extra Family' . . . ," Allen wrote, "insisted on trying to squeeze in between the Middle Pond Family and the Dike Pair, a boundary that was already jealously guarded. Again and again the two newcomers were chased, chiefly by the completely intolerant male of the Middle Family. Sometimes, during these chases, he would bear down on the lone female on the wing, force her into the air, and then harry her mercilessly, flying close on her tail for a mile or more. The fatherless youngster would fly also, but the chase always passed it by and an hour or more was often required for the homeless female to join her offspring again.

"Eventually the Extra Family spent much of its time in wet swales in the oak brush, beyond the limits of regular territories, where they were seldom bothered by other Whoopers. From these observations we decided that the presence of the male of a pair is essential to normal establishment of a territory and, further, that the insistence of the Extra Family on a site between the Dike and Middle Pond might indicate that the female had family connections with one of those areas. Perhaps the irate male of the Middle Family was her own father!"

However, not all meetings between crane families are hostile. Once, for example, Allen watched two adjoining families perform a strange ceremony for which he could not account:

"From the shelter of a live-oak thicket overlooking the flats I saw six Whooping Cranes close together in a bed of salt flat grass. . . . The first look showed them to be . . . two pairs and their rusty-plumaged young-of-the-year. They were some twenty-five yards apart, but as we watched the two males . . . separated themselves from their families and strutted slowly towards each other. Their strides were exaggerated and stiff, the wings dragging slightly, . . . their whole manner seemingly formal and almost self-conscious. . . . They came on until only a yard separated them, then stopped and looked about them. One dropped his head in a feeding movement and the other did likewise. But whatever emotion it was that spurred them on was strong medicine. They came within less than two feet of each other and repeated the feeding movement. Then both retreated a couple of feet. Suddenly they were close together again, and simultaneously their heads came up, bills pointing skyward, wings drooped, plumes raised over tail and back. Across the gray, misty flats we heard the thrilling trumpet call of the Whooping Crane. . . . After the first blast, during which the two males had their heads almost together, the females joined in, their posture the same as that of the males. The two young birds, standing idly on the outskirts of this performance, seemed to have no interest in the proceedings. . . . The males repeated their performance without the females' cooperation, then drew away from each other in a curious circling walk, heads down as if feeding. After a little, the males came together again, bowing this time, in short, stiff little nods. . . . They stood, finally, with their crimson crowns almost touching, bowing so low that their bills went back under the breast feathers and very nearly between the legs. . . .

"This remarkable show lasted over a period of 50 minutes, after which the two families calmly separated, each withdrawing into its own territory. The location of the demonstration had been the exact boundary between the two territorial claims."

Two families, each with young, meet in neutral territory at Aransas. The males greet each other ceremoniously.

8

When the Middle Pond Family arrived at Aransas their youngster was approximately five months old. It had learned to fly perhaps only six weeks before and yet had been able to follow its parents across more than two thousand miles of alien territory. On the ground it still looked small and awkward. Its wings, pinkish buff and cinnamon splotched with dull white, appeared too big for the rest of its rusty-plumaged body. Its head bristled with reddish feathers, giving a gawky, callow appearance that reminded Allen of an overly tall twelve-year-old boy whose hair needs brushing. But on the wing it would suddenly seem as large and capable as the adults. It had no trouble keeping up with them as they skimmed across the salt flats, and it landed with what Allen called "at least a simulation of dignity, to explore, with expert and solicitous guidance, the many wonders of their new habitation."

During the winter Allen was able to watch the young bird's maturation. In the first weeks it trailed closely after its parents. The female and young particularly were always side by side. The youngster's main interest was food, and at first it was fed almost entirely by the parents. (If there is only one youngster, the female takes on most of the feeding, Allen found, although the male will also offer it morsels from time to time. If there are twins, it later became evident, both parents care for both youngsters, but each is inclined to have a favorite to which most attention is devoted.)

At first the adult cranes feed the young by actually placing morsels, which they have broken into suitably small pieces, in the youngster's beak. Later the adult merely catches the prey, breaks it up, and places it before the youngster. By January the young crane has learned to search for its own food, with supplementary handouts still welcome, and by February it is feeding itself almost entirely. By this time, too, it is beginning to look like an adult, with the reddish plumage dropping away and being replaced by gleaming white.

Until the prenuptial dances of the parents become intense, in March or April, family life is orderly and calm. By that time the young crane has gained considerable confidence and taken experimental trips off on its

Young whooper landing in shallow water displays its seven-foot wingspread. At six months, young are still partly reddish in color.

own. Nevertheless it quite evidently comes as a shock when, almost without warning, its parents' attitude changes and the painful process of weaning begins.

As Allen saw it: "One day, the young hopeful who has been so carefully guarded and nurtured for so many weeks, suddenly becomes a source of annoyance. Its own mother turns on the bewildered creature and drives it from her presence. The male, in his turn, chases it too, sometimes flying after the poor youngster for a mile or so before leaving it to its own, uncertain devices."

However, the tie between parents and young has not yet been totally severed. When it is time to migrate, the parents recall the young one to their side, and the three, a family once more, migrate together. Somewhere in the north a final parting occurs, but just when or where no one knows.

The dance of the whooping crane is a justly celebrated performance that has long fascinated human beings because of its eerie resemblance to some human rites of spring. It is not peculiar to whoopers alone. Sandhills and other cranes perform a very similar ballet. Allen believed that the dance has an emotional basis and becomes more frequent and intense as the birds' sexual cycle progresses through its various stages to full breeding condition. It may then serve to strengthen and cement the bond between the pair. There are other times, however, when the cranes dance simply as a physical and emotional outlet, a means of releasing tension. Later, when Allen was able to watch nesting birds, he saw a bird, relieved from duty, arise after a long, wearying spell on the nest, walk a short distance, and then silently whirl and leap in a solitary dance.

Allen saw the first signs of a new breeding cycle at Aransas in late December or early January. At first only one bird of a pair would begin a dance, leaping into the air, flapping its wings and bowing, but then quickly settle down again. As the season progressed its mate joined in. Allen described a brief but complete dance thus: "The 26th [of January] was warm and clear, in contrast to the wet and chilly weather of January 10. The same pair that we had watched in a partial dance on the earlier date were observed moving slowly along the far bank of Middle Pond. Suddenly one bird (the male?) began bowing his head and flapping his wings. At the same time he leaped stiffly into the air, an amazing bounce on stiffened legs that carried him nearly three feet off the ground. In the air he threw his head back so that the bill pointed skyward, neck arched over his back. Throughout this leap the great wings were constantly flapping, their long black flight feathers in striking contrast to the dazzling white of the rest of the plumage. The second bird (the female?) was facing the first when he reached the ground after completing the initial bounce. She ran forward a few steps, pumping her head up and down and flapping her wings. Then both birds leaped into the air, wings flapping, necks doubled up over their backs, legs thrust downward stiffly. Again they leaped, bouncing as if on pogo sticks. On the ground they ran towards each other, bowing and spreading their huge wings. Then another leap! The climax was almost frantic, both birds leaping two and three times in succession. Quickly it was all over, after about four minutes, and an extended period of preening followed."

Family group at start of dance.

Male and female in initial dance postures.

Leaps and head bows of a full dance.

The male leaps over the female.

Male continues to dance, but the female has stopped and the young bird pays no attention.

As the day of migration draws near, the birds' emotions become increasingly hair-trigger. Any small excitement can provoke a dance, as when Allen saw a male crane leap to threaten a group of intruding ducks, and suddenly transmute these leaps into the pirouettes of a dance.

On April 3, 1948, just a few days prior to migration, Allen watched his now familiar Middle Pond Family in a typical display. "On this particular day the female was more interested in dancing than the male. While he fed, she and the now well-grown youngster were bathing, the

As migration nears, tempers are hair-trigger. Any excitement can provoke a sudden display.

offspring imitating the movements of the female. They were standing in water about 15 inches deep. The female would crouch hesitantly, like a bather cautiously feeling the water with an exploratory toe.

"Then she would dip all the way under, except for her head and neck, splashing up and down, shaking her partly open wings, wiggling her tail and throwing her head about so that her crown stroked the feathers of her back. The immature Whooper imitated all this awkwardly. Then both birds stood and shook themselves vigorously, flapped their wings, wiggled their tails, ran their bills through their dripping primaries and began jumping up and down. The male kept on with his feeding. Then the female began leaping and flapping in a wide circle, running as she leaped. The immature watched and started to follow suit. The female turned and, with head lowered as in an attack, chased the youngster. She chased it repeatedly. Though obviously bewildered, the youngster continued following her and attempting to leap and circle as she did, wings flapping. After a little, the male, looking up from his searching, walked towards the female, leaped and beat his wings a few times. But no complete dance resulted. The routine of the long winter months was nearly broken. There was an air of excitement, of impending change. The cranes seemed almost as if poised, ready, waiting for the sound of a starting gun."

Unfortunately, not all the events that Allen observed on the marsh were as orderly as the private lives of the cranes. In the course of the two winters that he spent at Aransas, Allen became increasingly distressed as more and more threats pressed in upon the refuge.

Oil, under the water or on land, was a sword always poised over the refuge. In early 1948, Allen learned that the Western Natural Gas Company of Houston, on a sublease from Continental Oil, was preparing to drill on the sand flats in prime whooping-crane territory. This, it seemed, might be the beginning of the final disaster. Allen telephoned John Baker in New York. A conference was arranged with the company's officers at which Allen and Baker explained the probable consequences to the cranes. To its great credit the company saw the point. While they did not abandon the plan entirely, the officers agreed to drill in summer when the cranes would be absent, and to take other precautions designed to protect the cranes' winter habitat.

Meanwhile, it became increasingly obvious to Allen that poachers could come and go on the refuge almost as they pleased. In March, 1948, someone—who was never caught—came onto the refuge and shot the flightless female of the Summer Pair. Allen found the bird lying wounded on the salt marsh. As Allen approached she managed to get up and struggle into the brush, but he had seen that her breast was stained with blood. The next day Allen and Refuge Manager Keefer found her again. They caught her and carried her to refuge headquarters, hoping that a veterinary might save her, but the bird died within a few hours. In addition to the old wound crippling her wing, there was a recent bullet wound through the trachea.

Allen reported her death in a long memorandum to Washington. Then, in a "Progress Report" he made a vehement plea for better protection for the whooping cranes. "Direct protection," he wrote, "is a first essential. There is no point providing a habitat if no wild life remains to live in it. In the case of the whooping crane every loss is a calamity and every calamity is a long step toward the extinction that we are making it our business to prevent."

Allen reviewed the way in which the whooping cranes' security had first been breached by the waterway: "The cranes are disturbed every day by lines of great barges that bear down on these ancestral shores, pushed by throbbing, purposeful tug boats; or by fleets of fast-moving shrimp boats, sending up a swirl and wash of churned water that engulfs the *alterniflora* on the banks and scatters the schools of small fry in whirling eddies of sudden and unfamiliar motion."

Allen told how he had often watched whooping cranes, feeding quietly on the shore of the refuge, forced to fly as oil barges or shrimp boats bore down on them. He cited a specific episode in which a pair of feeding whoopers were so repeatedly disturbed by boats that they gave up feeding and flew to a different strip of shore, only to be harried by a light airplane: "It continued to dive and circle the poor birds until they rose and flew toward the outside edge of their territory." In doing so the whoopers passed directly over a fleet of fishing boats in the canal where there might easily have been a gunner unable to tell a crane from a pelican.

There was ample evidence that there were gunners aboard the boats that passed within easy range of the feeding cranes. Once Allen saw a boy on a passing shrimp boat fire at ducks and feeding whooping cranes. The whoopers, sounding their loud alarm notes, took wing, and escaped. On another occasion, as Allen was watching the East Family of cranes he saw a barge approach. On deck was a man with a shotgun in his hands, firing at ducks along the canal. Luckily, the whooping cranes were just out of range and did not fly, but they could as easily have been at the edge of the canal. At the end of the 1947 shooting season, Allen found a duck blind on the refuge within the territory of a family of whooping cranes. The litter of empty shells around it showed that it had seen considerable use without being noticed by refuge personnel. "I want to make it clear," Allen wrote, "that I have no intention of censuring Refuge personnel or the Service . . . on the other hand if some of these facts are known . . . it should be possible to overcome many of the inevitable barriers. . . ." He then listed measures that might give the cranes the extra protection they needed. The most urgent problem, Allen felt, was a full-time patrol of the Waterway. At that time the refuge possessed no boat, nor even a place to bring one ashore through the shallows. Allen proposed that a channel be dredged and the refuge equipped with a small, fast boat so that a refuge patrolman could overtake and disarm poachers.

Allen's memorandum also discussed ways in which the cranes could be lured from dangerous proximity to the Waterway by supplementary feeding. He suggested that grain crops be planted for them and brushy plots burned over regularly to make acorns and insects accessible. He stressed the increasingly serious menace of oil pollution of the refuge waters and the need for stronger legal power to prevent it. Finally, he took up the matter of "improvement" of the refuge for the benefit of ducks and geese, pointing out that any tampering with the water systems of the refuge that would allow fresh water to flood the marshes and lessen their salinity would be a blow to the food supply of the cranes.

Washington officials of the Fish and Wildlife Service make the decisions ultimately carried out in the field, but as in all bureaucratic systems, orders travel a route that is often long and complex. The service's refuges are not administered directly from Washington but through a system of five regional headquarters, each responsible for all the refuges within its area. The Aransas Refuge is the responsibility of the regional director in Albuquerque, New Mexico. Washington therefore replied to Allen's memorandum by saying that his recommendations would be given close attention. The problem of patrol would be taken up with the regional director with the request that Aransas personnel redouble their efforts.

What Washington didn't answer, of course, was the question implicit in all of Allen's warnings and recommendations: How far out of its way would the service go in its efforts to preserve the whooping cranes? How much of its limited funds should it spend on them, if it meant neglect of other urgent needs? With the Aransas Refuge serving to protect most of its animal inhabitants quite adequately, how much additional should be done for such difficult, finicky guests as the cranes—guests who might at any moment take it into their heads to depart?

9

Shortly after his initial visit in 1946 to the New Orleans Zoo to see Josephine, the captive whooping crane, Allen began negotiations to bring her together with Pete, the one-eyed whooper that had been the guest of the Gothenburg Gun Club in Nebraska since 1936. He wrote to the custodian of each bird, carefully explaining the critical situation of the species and the great benefit to the cause of the cranes if the meeting of the two birds should prove fruitful. Both George Douglass, superintendent of the New Orleans Zoo and the spokesman for the Gun Club replied that they would be glad to cooperate by lending their birds.

The next step was to find a suitable place in which to attempt to breed them. Allen toyed with, and discarded, the idea of turning the flightless birds loose at Aransas and letting nature take its course. A second possibility, that of caging them at Aransas in a large enclosure, would involve persuading the Fish and Wildlife Service to spend a considerable sum to build a fence. There was a third possibility—to have the birds kept at a zoo where, presumably, there would be the advantage of expert care. Among the possibilities were Chicago's Lincoln Park Zoo, which had a large flying cage, or the St. Louis Zoo, which had had considerable success in breeding rare birds. Fred Stark, director of the small but excellent San Antonio Zoo, was also notable for his interest in aviculture. Finally of course there was the Audubon Park Zoo, which had the advantage that Josephine was already accustomed to life there.

During the summer of 1947 Allen and John Baker of the Audubon Society discussed the pros and cons by mail. Washington was cool to the idea of building a large pen at Aransas. The northern zoos had the disadvantage of cold climate. Allen had been far from impressed by the upkeep of the New Orleans Zoo. On the other hand John Baker felt that it would be tactless to ask George Douglass to send his crane to San Antonio, also a southern zoo. In November, 1947, John Baker visited New Orleans and met Douglass for the first time. He found him a cordial host, and eager to cooperate in the breeding experiment. "You'll like him," he wrote Allen at one point, and in another letter admonished him, "For Pete's sake, don't tell him his zoo isn't good enough!"

From Aransas, Allen wrote Baker that he now agreed that because of the difficulty of getting a proper enclosure at Aransas the best plan would be to send Pete to join Josephine at New Orleans.

It was a solution that Allen accepted without much enthusiasm. In a letter to Baker he apologized for "being difficult." He conceded that "despite a rather varied diet and exposure to crowds, noise and carbon monoxide," Josephine seemed to be in fine condition, but he insisted that a better cage, with running water, seclusion, more natural food, and enough headroom for dancing, would be essential to the success of the venture. Shortly thereafter Baker wrote Allen that Pete would arrive at New Orleans about December 15. Douglass had agreed to build two new, isolated pens. If things failed to work out well at New Orleans, Douglass would send both birds to Aransas.

The tricky business of organizing the transfer of Pete was handled by George P. Vierheller of the St. Louis Zoo. Pete arrived at the Audubon Park Zoo in late December, 1947. His meeting with Josephine has not been recorded; but in early February, Baker wrote Allen relaying word from Douglass that the captives had been put together and were getting along well, although they showed no great interest in each other.

On March 15, 1948, Allen left Aransas to see for himself what was going on at New Orleans. What he saw there and how he felt about it is recorded in a memorandum dated March 29, and addressed to the Fish and Wildlife Service in Washington:

"On March 17th [1948] . . . I visited George Douglass at Audubon Park, New Orleans, and observed the two captive whooping cranes in their special enclosure on the grounds of the Audubon Park Zoo. I would be a dissembling coward if I did not admit that I was shocked and distressed by what I saw. The two birds are merely existing, shut up in a ridiculously small pen scarcely large enough for a pair of tame ducks. The pen is located in the 'backyard' of the zoo, close to rubbish and without anything even remotely resembling isolation from noise and casual, disinterested disturbances. The floor of the pen is covered more or less by short grass, now well trampled. There is no natural water, but the original pans of water have been replaced by metal washtubs filled with dirty water. The bottom of the wire does not meet the ground all around, and we saw rat tracks running through the mud around the tubs, indicating that rats come and go at will.

"There is no shade except the wood shack at one end. Mr. Douglass said that both birds go inside this shack on occasion. There is a bed of straw on the floor.

"The head room and ground space are both entirely inadequate for whooping cranes that have been placed together for the purpose of pairing off and, presumably, breeding. Even worse, their diet is almost certainly a guarantee that they will never breed again! Each bird is being fed the following daily amounts:

"1 and ½ lbs. scratch grain, 1 and ½ lbs. fish (cut in small pieces), 1 and ½ lbs. bread.

"Some time ago I wrote Mr. Douglass suggesting *live* crayfish and blue crabs. The blue crab, in particular, is unusually rich in nutritious values, including a high protein content and a wealth of vitamins A, B, and C. He recently offered a half dozen crayfish to the birds but they 'were too excited' to pay any attention to them. He wanted to know if soft shelled crabs were 'anything like' blue crabs! While I was present he called a nearby café and ordered soft-shelled crabs from their deep-freeze with the idea of 'testing' my claim that the birds would take blue crabs and improve their general tone and condition on such a diet. Wow!! I tried to explain what poor food value is contained in ordinary store bread under these circumstances. I also attempted to describe the outward signs that demonstrate good physical condition in the species and especially the increasing gonadal development. The soft part color changes that I have noted in my wild birds are very definite, and I assured Mr. Douglass that until their *environment* and *diet* were greatly changed he would see no soft part color changes in these captive birds and could expect no breeding. I have a feeling that all this was mere mumbo-jumbo as far as he was concerned.

"Douglass seems to mean well, but he should not have charge of those precious birds! They both look bad, have poor color, general lack of tone. The Nebraska bird is highly nervous, almost hysterical (its original enclosure in Gothenburg was large, without a roof and was traversed by channels of the Platte River from which he secured live fish, frogs, etc.). I fear for the survival of both birds, particularly the Nebraska bird.

"To expect them—*if* male and female—to pair and breed and deposit a set of fertile eggs under the conditions described, is nothing short of idiotic. I must be absolutely honest and outspoken on this subject because it is too important to misrepresent or waste time being polite about or soft pedaling in any way in this type of private communication. Those birds must be moved and moved soon. Their present condition is a disgraceful thing! The species has suffered much but those two birds represent the lowest rung. I could have wept when I saw them, if I hadn't been so numb with anger and shame.

"I have an immediate suggestion. Directly southeast of the Aransas headquarters buildings and adjacent to Webb Point is an extensive salt flat marsh. Wind tides keep its ponds supplied with crabs, fish and other marine life from the open bay. In back of, and to the west of the salt flat area are heavy growths of *typha* and other fresh water aquatics, creating a splendid nesting environment. The location is sufficiently extensive to be isolated and yet near enough headquarters to be easily watched. It is far removed from the Intracoastal Canal.

"All that is needed to make this area a safe and adequate location for the two captive birds is some additional fencing. I have discussed the suitability of the habitat with Lynch, Keefer and others and the fencing problem with Keefer and other refuge personnel. All are enthusiastic about the location and willing to cooperate fully in working out plans for creating a practical enclosure.

"I have invited Douglass to come over here and he may do so soon. He will, I think, be eager to get rid of the two birds. He realizes, I believe, that they are more of a responsibility than he can handle with the facilities and experience at his command. When I show him the cat-tail marsh and adjacent salt flat ponds and outline our plans for an extensive enclosure I feel that he will cooperate whole-heartedly. He may wish to retain 'title' to his crane, so be it. We can keep it here more or less indefinitely and eventually, if no breeding occurs after several seasons and he wants it returned, it will not be difficult to catch."

Allen's report got prompt action in Washington. Within a few days the Chief of the Division of Wildlife Research, to whom Allen had addressed himself, wrote that he would urge that the birds be moved to Aransas in accordance with Allen's recommendations. Shortly thereafter the service ordered a wire fence nine feet high, enclosing the tract of a hundred and fifty acres that Allen had described. The fence would cost two thousand dollars. Until it was completed, however, Josephine and Pete would have to remain at New Orleans.

Douglass agreed readily enough to send the pair of cranes to Aransas. John Baker, who had taken on the task of keeping pleasant relations between all parties, wrote to thank him for permitting "the indefinite loan of your bird." "Certainly it should be understood," he wrote, "that if the experiment be a definite failure, your bird would be returned to you; moreover, that should your bird, unfortunately die, or be injured while at Aransas, there would, of course, be no claim made by your Park Commission."

With relief Allen returned to the work of completing his notes on the biology of the cranes' habitat. A primary object of Allen's two years of study was to discover exactly what whooping cranes eat, a subject at that time completely undocumented. As Allen attacked the problem, he found himself in the frustrating position of watching the birds feed and yet being unable to see what was actually going down their throats. The first step was a painstaking study of the flora and fauna of the marsh. Then, from watching the cranes and studying the ground they had covered, he was able to deduce a great deal. A certain diagram of whooping-crane tracks accompanied by scattered claws and shells

The male is watchful while mate and young whooping crane feed. Their behavior en famille *makes it easy to tell sexes apart.*

showed where the birds had dug blue crabs out of their burrows. Elsewhere the birds had walked in a straight line, probing to right and left to pluck tiny marine worms from the soft mud. Eventually Allen was able to make a list of the main items on the whooper's menu. He felt that the blue crab was of such importance to the cranes' survival that the bureau should make a special study of its life cycle and make sure its numbers do not diminish. Next in importance are mud shrimp, annelid worms, and a miscellany of small marine creatures. Small fish appear on the list, but the cranes do not depend on them as they do on the crustaceans. When the whoopers feed in fresh water they are partial to crayfish, frogs, and aquatic insects. On land they will pursue grasshoppers, or almost any small "chance prey," including reptiles and birds. Vegetable food, in Allen's opinion, is not normally a major part of the cranes' diet, but they accept it on occasion.

As Allen watched the cranes in their final weeks before departure for the north, late in the spring of 1948, he happened to witness the next episode in the life story of Crip, the survivor of the Summer Pair. Crip had of course been single since the shooting of his mate in March. In April, as members of the flock began leaving, it seemed that Crip would be doomed to summer alone. Then, on April 17, a clear, bright spring day, Allen chanced to be walking down Rattlesnake Road when he heard a whooping-crane call. "A single bird was in flight, headed north," Allen wrote. "On the far bank was Crip calling to it. The single bird answered, circled, and came to earth. She descended within ten feet of Crip. He walked off with dignity and she followed." Crip's call must have been a persuasive one, for his new lady stayed by his side all through the long, hot summer.

During the winter Allen had been making plans for a second trip to the North in search of whooping-crane nests. A number of tips had come in. A Royal Canadian Air Force pilot wrote that he had seen cranes of "tremendous size" just south of the point where the Mackenzie River flows into the Arctic Ocean, a spot almost a thousand miles north and west of the areas that had previously been searched. A second suggestion mentioned Lac Le Martre, north of Great Slave Lake; a third recommended the western shore of Hudson Bay.

These ideas fitted into a manageable pattern. The complete failure of previous searches in more southerly areas led Allen to think of territory farther north. There is a natural flyway for ducks, geese, and swans that channels northward along the Athabaska, Slave, and Mackenzie River routes. It seemed possible the cranes followed it as well.

As it happened, the Wildlife Services of both the United States and Canada were interested in getting estimates of waterfowl populations along the arctic coasts. Again Allen arranged to join Robert Smith, the pilot-biologist with whom he had flown the previous summer. The two men could combine their missions so as to count waterfowl and at the same time look for whooping cranes in the Far North.

In May, Allen drove from Texas to Regina, Saskatchewan, where he met Smith. On June 3 the two men started off in the little Widgeon belonging to the United States Government. Again they flew to Fort Smith, unaware that they were, comparatively speaking, within a stone's throw of the hidden target, and flew on, almost a thousand miles farther north, to make what Allen called "a painstaking, low-altitude hunt—lake by lake, muskeg by muskeg."

In a month of flying, Allen and Smith covered more than fourteen thousand miles, going as far north as Point Barrow, Alaska, and the shores of the Arctic Ocean. In all that vast country they found not a single clue that might unlock the secret. The miserable climax of these futile miles was a forced landing in an arctic lake. For sixteen hours, until the wind dropped, the two men stood in icy water, holding the wings of the light plane to prevent it from being battered to pieces on the rocky shore.

When the trip ended, Allen felt utterly baffled and discouraged. He wrote: "Once more we failed to locate the nesting grounds. Our only consolation is the realization that wherever this unknown place may be it is evidently hidden not only from us, but from anyone who might disturb the birds or do them harm. One thing seems certain: the place we are looking for is in virtual truth a lost land. It is probable that no human being, white or aboriginal, lives there, at least not in spring or summer. This would account for the unknown character of this enchanted spot, a never-never land that has resisted discovery by a naturalist since earliest times."

After this second summer of failure, Allen gave up the idea of further organized searches, since he now had no idea of where to look. There was always the hope, though, that someone else might acidentally come across new clues. Both the Canadian and United States Fish and Wildlife Service men in the north had been made thoroughly aware of the great whooping-crane-in-the-haystack hunt, and would be alert for any sign of the birds as they made their rounds.

Because Allen's field research at Aransas was now complete, on his return from Canada he went, not to Texas, but to his home in Florida, to write the monograph whose findings and recommendations, he earnestly hoped, would help the Fish and Wildlife Service to help the whooping cranes to survive. Checking up on the summer's events at the refuge, he learned that it had been a hot, dry summer. Crip and his new mate had ranged widely in search of acceptable habitat, but had nevertheless come through the summer in good condition.

In November, 1948, the flock of twenty-eight that had migrated in the spring returned. They had brought back three youngsters, but three adults had fallen by the wayside, neatly canceling the gain. With Crip and his mate there was now a flock of thirty whooping cranes. This was a far healthier figure than the low twenties of only a few years before, but it was one less than the count of the autumn of the previous year. As Allen sat down to work, it was with the sense that the whoopers were still operating on the thinnest of margins but that given any sort of chance they could and would survive.

10

The enclosure at Aransas that was to receive the two captive whooping cranes was ready in October, 1948. The fence surrounded 150 acres that combined brackish marsh typical of whooping-crane winter territory with a freshwater cattail marsh similar to the whooping cranes' natural nesting habitat. It was the nearest thing possible to freedom. Meanwhile, Allen and Baker had managed to have Josephine and Pete transferred from New Orleans to the San Antonio Zoo. Fred Stark, its director, one of the most skillful aviculturists in the country, has successfully bred several species of rare cranes. He pinioned the captives' crippled wings in order to reduce the chances of their injuring themselves in an attempt to fly, and fed them a rich diet calculated to put them in breeding condition. Finally the birds were trucked to Aransas, and released. Much to Allen's gratification, they settled down almost immediately. They took up the business of leading normal whooping-crane lives—stalking blue crabs, fishing for shrimps, and searching the grass for frogs and insects—as though their freedom had never been interrupted. Josephine was already relatively tame, but Pete had always maintained an aloof manner during his twelve years of captivity. Now, however, he made friends with Mrs. Keefer, the wife of the refuge manager. Pete and Josephine came up to the fence every day for a ration of corn soaked in wheat-germ oil, and also, apparently, for the pleasure of Mrs. Keefer's company.

"As long as she stays there they stand, preen and snooze," Keefer wrote to Allen. "When she leaves they move off. They know her voice and when she talks to them, answer with a sort of guttural, rolling sound like they were trying to 'purr.' They will eat from her hand, but only from hers; not mine."

In December Josephine and Pete performed a prenuptial dance. This hopeful news was relayed to Allen in Florida, to John Baker in New York, and to Fish and Wildlife officials in Washington and Canada. Rarely has the announcement of a betrothal been better received.

The dancing of the captives became more intense during March and April. Then, on April 27, at the hour when both birds usually came to the fence for their ration of corn, only one bird appeared. Keefer wondered if possibly the missing bird were on a nest. The next day again only one bird appeared. On the third day Keefer was able to see Pete crouching in the cattails while Josephine came up for corn. On April 30 Keefer went into the enclosure and sneaked toward the clump of cattails that sheltered Pete. As Keefer approached, Pete whooped a warning and rose to drive back the intruder. Keefer was pecked on the arm and hand before he retreated. He had seen the nest. It contained a single egg.

Four days later Keefer again approached the nest to photograph it. Both parents "raised an awful fuss, whooping and scolding." Josephine pecked at his right thumb, drawing blood, then grabbed his sleeve and

Josephine's first, ill-fated nest was hidden away among cattails on the Aransas marsh.

tried to pull him away. She finally pecked him, hard, on top of the head. Keefer got his picture, but was glad to retreat. During the commotion Pete stood on the nest, hovering excitedly. There were now two eggs.

Allen, who was in Florida at the time, hurried to Texas and arrived on May 12. He posted himself in an observation tower overlooking the nesting area. There he spent each day, from dawn to dusk, keeping a minute-to-minute record of the activities of the nesting cranes.

The nest was a flat mound constructed chiefly of salt-flat grass, with some strands of cattail leaves and sea oxeye. Almost six feet across, but no more than ten inches high, it was well hidden in a dense growth of cattail, and surrounded by water that was at first almost a foot deep, but later went down to a few inches. The parents took turns incubating. At first there were usually six nest reliefs during the day. As the weather grew warmer, the birds exchanged duties more often. The male spent more time on the eggs during the day than did the female, averaging two hours at a spell to her one and a half hours. Overall, Pete did more than 70 percent of daytime incubation. Although it was impossible to see what happened at night, Allen assumed that Josephine was mostly on the eggs while her mate stood guard.

In his monograph Allen made this report: "When the incubating bird stood on the nest it was in plain view, from this vantage point, but when it settled on the eggs it was extremely difficult to see and was often out of sight completely. However, with the aid of a 19.5 spottingscope its movements generally could be followed without much loss of detail.

"The male was sometimes extremely restless and particular about his position on the eggs. On May 12th, after relieving the female at 8:12 A.M., he did not stir until 9:04 A.M. Then he stood and rearranged the position of his feet and of the eggs four times in the next 45 minutes. At 9:55 A.M., with the female standing close by, he walked off the nest, possibly to drink, and was back again within a few seconds. Although he stayed on the nest, except for momentary excursions of a few seconds each, until 12:55 P.M., the male rose and fussed with the eggs and the nest five more times. Once he added more nesting material. Some of the excursions were evidently for water.

"Also on May 12th, at dusk (7:10 P.M.), the male was on the eggs and the female, standing near the nest, raised her wings and jabbed with her bill at something in the cattails. The male remained motionless. Four minutes later the female sounded an alarm note and ran, wings partly opened, towards something in back of the nest. The incubating male never moved. Then we saw a large doe . . . retreating rapidly with the enraged female in pursuit. The male, low on the nest, sat like a statue.

"On occasion the incubating bird seemed to grow extremely weary. On May 14th, after the usual noontime relief, during which the two birds might exchange places on the eggs twice, or even three times, within a half hour, the male resumed his incubation at 1:30 P.M. . . . and when the female did not come near the nest by 4:20 P.M., the male simply stood and with bill open, as if very hot and tired, walked off. The female, who was perhaps 20 yards off, immediately started directly towards the nest, covering the eggs two minutes later, after arranging them to suit her. . . .

"In both leaving and approaching the nest, the free bird nearly always followed a devious route through the cattails, disappearing for a space and then emerging 40 or 50 yards to one side. Once in the open this caution diminished and . . . the bird might dance briefly, but silently, or relax enough to bathe in a pool of fresh water. . . .

"The bird that was relieved at the nest often showed real pleasure at its release. Once Josephine stepped off the mound and Pete took over, . . . Josephine stood for a moment and then went running and skipping off toward the open marsh, her wings flapping gaily. Another time she walked as far as the nearest salt pond and, standing on the bank, did a wonderful little dance—apparently through sheer exuberance—twirling and leaping around and around, dipping her body low, wings extended, and then leaping sideways.

"In addition to feeding, the free bird spent a lot of time coping with real or imaginary dangers. One day when Pete was probing around on the higher ground, where painted buntings were singing beautifully from the mesquite brush, he came on a large rattlesnake, half coiled on a patch of bare ground. Pete walked up to him and started dancing up and down, wings flapping. Around and around the snake he went, the reptile's head turning slowly to watch him. After a few minutes Pete broke the impasse by suddenly walking off. On another occasion, however, he attacked a large cotton mouth moccasin, beat it to death by stabbing furiously at its head, and then swallowed it entire. . . .

"Most guard duty however consisted of chasing off other birds, especially American egrets, snowy egrets, Ward's herons, Louisiana herons, and roseate spoonbills. The Ward's heron and American egret were a particular anathema to him. At times the male would chase egrets the entire length of the salt pond, or nearly a mile. He seemed more cautious in attacking Ward's herons, but never failed to evict them, no matter how far from the nest the chase carried him.

"On May 21st, the male was relieved at 2:52 P.M. and walked immediately to the salt pond, where he chased a group of American egrets. When they simply flew to the far side of the pond he charged after them again. At this juncture a Ward's heron flew across the pond and came down on the west shore. The male turned from the egrets and gave his full attention to the Ward's. He actually *whooped* at it several times, strutting very stiffly and with an air of great dignity. Then he lowered his spear-like head and neck and charged, running with huge strides and flapping his wings rapidly, fairly skipping across the surface of the water. The heron, glaring at the male in what seemed a very disconcerted manner, stood his ground until the juggernaut was almost upon him. Then he rose and flew. The male, with only one complete wing, usually ended his charge at this point, slowing and shortening his stride, using his wings as a brake, arching his neck until it looked like that of a swan, and coming to a rather abrupt but wholly dignified stop. Two hapless egrets were standing nearby, uncertain whether to stay or fly, and the male settled the issue for them by walking towards them, his head high, his manner aggressive. The Ward's heron, discouraged, flew out of the enclosure. After another moment, the male charged the two egrets, and they quickly followed the Ward's. When every last intruder had been sent packing and the entire pond and salt flat were his, the male strutted back towards the nest, his solemn grandeur a joy to behold. . . .

"The female, a younger bird and in finer plumage, always looked clean and neat. The old male, from so much chasing through mud and water, was usually dirty and ruffled-looking. Sometimes, after a series of exhausting chases, he walked back towards the nest dripping wet and black underneath from the splashing mud. He was a game old warrior and did the best he could."

The exact period of incubation of whooping-crane eggs was unknown, but there is usually a correlation between the volume of an egg and the time it takes to hatch. On this basis Allen guessed that Josephine's eggs should hatch on about the thirty-third day. But on the twenty-fourth day the routine of incubation was suddenly broken. Allen, watching in the tower, saw both birds acting strangely. They got on and off the nest in a restless fashion and poked anxiously at the eggs. Abruptly they left the nest, walked toward the open meadow together, and danced. Allen descended the tower and crept toward the nest. Josephine and Pete made no effort to stop him. He found the two eggs smashed—evidently by the parents. The remains were merely empty shells; the infertile contents dried up and futile.

Pete lived only another two months. At dawn on July 22 Josephine trumpeted in distress. The refuge manager, Julian Howard, who had taken Keefer's place, found her standing alone, whooping wildly. Pete lay dead, on his back, in shallow water. Postmortem showed no new injury. His death was ascribed to natural causes.

Since Josephine had shown herself willing and able to nest in captivity, it seemed urgent to find her another mate. Crip was the obvious candidate. He and his new mate had not nested, so Crip's potential was being wasted. Therefore, shortly after Pete's death Allen sent a memo to John Baker: "I strongly urge that our experiment be continued and that the first move should be to place Crip in the enclosure. Of course the odds are considerable that nothing will come of such a move, but it seems to me that at this stage of the game we can't very well afford to overlook any chances whatever. Even with a successful breeding next Spring the thread between survival and extinction remains very thin."

Washington agreed that Crip should be captured, but it was also decided to postpone the capture until cool weather. In early October a four-man posse chased Crip and his companion through the brush. Although the second bird was able to fly, it stayed at Crip's side until the men had almost closed in on them. Then it flew. Crip, struggling valiantly, was caught in a fishnet and released in Josephine's enclosure. Apparently Crip did not mourn his wild companion. To the satisfaction of all concerned, he and Josephine were compatible. Crip became tame quite quickly and soon joined Josephine at the fence at four each afternoon for dinner.

There was also satisfaction in the whooping-crane circle, which now engaged in a regular exchange of information between Aransas, Washington, New York, and Florida, when the entire complement of cranes made a safe return from Canada with four young birds. The flock in the autumn of 1949 was thirty-four, the highest number in Aransas records. Allen was especially elated that the cranes had made the round trip without a fatality. He felt that perhaps the publicity of previous years might at last be influencing the hunters who would otherwise have shot at the migrant whoopers.

The winter on the refuge was relatively serene. Fortunately, the oil well that had been drilled on the marsh during the summer was dry, and no new drilling on crane habitat was impending. Although there were now ten producing wells, they were safely distant from the marsh.

During the winter, as it became certain that the capture of Crip had been a success, the whooping-crane circle began to give serious thought to the idea of salvaging yet another bird as a potential breeder. This bird was the sole survivor of the White Lake colony to which Josephine had once belonged. Ever since the storm that had blown her and her companions out of the marsh five years earlier, John Lynch of the Fish and Wildlife Service had been keeping tabs on the small remnant that had returned. One by one this handful of birds dwindled. For the past two years Lynch had been able to find only a solitary bird. Everyone agreed that it should be captured, but how to do it was a perplexing problem. The bird ranged so widely that to lure it into a snare or trap seemed impractical. At length Allen and Lynch worked out a scheme to capture it by helicopter; their idea was to hover over the bird in such a way that the downdraft of the propellers would pin it to the ground. John Baker approved the project and so did Dr. Clarence Cottam, now the Assistant Director of the Fish and Wildlife Service, but Cottam warned Lynch: "Be careful! Biologists are expendable; whooping cranes are not."

On Saturday, March 11, 1950, a capture party assembled. Allen had arranged for the services of a helicopter and pilot. Lynch had the use of an ancient Stinson L-5. In addition to Lynch and Allen and the two pilots, the group included Nick Schexnayder, superintendent of Audubon's Rainey Wildlife Sanctuary south of Lafayette, Louisiana. The posse flushed the lone whooping crane from the marsh without too much difficulty, and then a wild air rodeo began. The Stinson managed to stay on the bird's tail as it twisted and turned, dived and soared. The crane's airspeed was clocked at forty-five miles an hour. Eventually the bird landed on the marsh and took cover in a clump of sawgrass. Allen and Schexnayder, in the helicopter, came to earth beside it. Both leaped out and grabbed the bird. In a moment they had a sack over its wings and its legs tied together. The captive seemed in good shape, considering what it had been through.

The men had planned to fly the bird to Aransas immediately, but bad weather suddenly made this impossible, so they decided to drive instead. The whooping crane, quickly named Mac in honor of the helicopter pilot, shared the back seat of Allen's sedan with Schexnayder. Lynch and Allen took turns driving through the night. For a while, as Allen drove, his companions fell asleep and began to snore. The crane evidently remained awake, for Allen heard it answer each snore with a low, guttural talking noise.

In the morning at Aransas they lifted the crane out of the car and prepared to turn it loose. To their dismay they found that the captive was in bad shape—too weak, in fact, to stand. It also occurred to the captors that this crane, unlike the Aransas whoopers, was accustomed to a freshwater environment and, in its weakened condition, might die of thirst on the brackish marsh. After considerable worried consultation, it was decided to pen the bird beside a small freshwater pond. While the refuge manager and his men hastily put up a fence, enclosing an acre or so, the others worked over the sick crane. The bird drank water and accepted small frogs that the men caught in the cattails. After its legs had been massaged to restore the circulation, the crane was able to stand, and it then allowed itself to be walked up and down the road. When the bird seemed to have picked up enough strength to look after itself, the flight feathers of one wing were clipped and it was turned loose in the enclosure. Then, hoping for the best, Allen and Lynch left the crane in the care of Howard, and returned to their homes.

On Monday, the second day of his captivity, Mac still would not feed himself, but walked ceaselessly along the fence of his pen, trying to get out. At length Howard decided the bird might do better if turned loose. He force-fed him and then took him to a freshwater area and released him. From here Mac walked a half a mile into the domain of a pair of wild whoopers, who attacked him. Mac, because of his clipped wing, was unable to escape. On Tuesday Howard found the bird on the marsh, wet, dazed, and with blood from gashes on his head staining his feathers. Howard carried the wounded crane to his house, where he put him in the kitchen, and sent for Fred Stark. Stark treated the wounds, which turned out not to be serious. Again the main problem was the bird's refusal to eat, and after force-feeding him again, Howard decided that it would be best to turn Mac loose. This time he released him at a freshwater lake far from any other cranes. Here Mac seemed to get along well enough. Howard saw him from time to time during the spring and summer. Then, on September 1, Howard found Mac's corpse by the lake. The cause of death, whether injuries, disease, or improper environment, was not determined, but autopsy showed the bird to have been a female.

The death of Mac left Josephine the sole representative of the Louisiana strain of whooping cranes. No one knows if the Louisiana whoopers' ability to nest without migration was a trait determined by genetic makeup, but it is considered quite likely that it was. If so, this trait could have been invaluable in saving the species. If it were possible to breed whooping cranes of sedentary habit, it would be far more likely that captive-bred birds could be acclimated to the wild to start new flocks of whooping cranes. Sedentary cranes could be protected with infinitely greater ease than birds that must fly the length of the continent twice each year. Thus the loss of the next-to-last Louisiana bird was more than the loss of one individual—it was the loss of precious genes and irreplaceable opportunity.

Robert Allen felt, bitterly, that here was an object lesson in the perils of ignorance in handling wild whooping cranes. From this time forward he opposed all proposals to capture any of the wild flock. He had many reasons for his conviction that it should not be attempted, but among the strongest was his fear that further experiments in capturing cranes could turn out as fatally as they had in the case of Mac. And, as he had said before, "Every loss is a long step toward the extinction we are making it our business to prevent."

11

In April, 1950, as the wild cranes were leaving the salt marshes of Aransas, Josephine and Crip built a nest. They built it far out on the open flats, amid short grass and in plain view, about a thousand feet from the tower. Newspaper stories announcing that the birds were nesting suddenly caught the public imagination. A flood of letters, wires, and telephone calls asking for news began to arrive at Aransas. Tourists from thirty-six states and from Canada and New Zealand visited the refuge, hoping for a glimpse of the celebrated birds. Julian Howard, the manager, found that his duties as host were taking a great deal of time. He also found it necessary to close the road to the marsh to all but refuge cars to prevent disturbance of the birds. Still the nesting cranes were occasionally bothered by trespassers who approached the nest site from the Waterway.

As interest in the nesting of the whooping cranes continued to mount, shedding a warm radiance of publicity over everyone associated with them, George Douglass, in the shadows of the New Orleans Zoo, began to grow restive. He expressed his discontent to John Baker, who had persuaded him to continue his "loan" of Josephine for another year after the death of Pete.

Again Baker begged him to allow the experiment to continue. On April 30 the *Times-Picayune* ran a story under the headline WHOOPING CRANE LAYS EGG—PARK WANTS RARE BIRD BACK. The story said in part: "Douglass said he hadn't been notified about the egg laying, but that the event was expected. He is anxious to get Josephine . . . home. He plans to swap her, on a loan basis, to a northern zoo for a panda: 'The folks there have never seen a whooping crane and our people haven't seen a panda. I expect our crane back after the egg is hatched so we can make the swap.' "

Meanwhile, at Aransas, Josephine and Crip continued the same diligent routine that Allen had recorded the year before. Allen, who was now at home in Florida finishing his monograph on the cranes, kept in close touch with Aransas, and came there on May 23 when the hatching was expected shortly. And indeed, on the very next day the birds' behavior changed as though a momentous event were at hand. Both birds seemed extremely tense. Josephine took on the brooding at ten in the morning and from then on scarcely moved. Allen and Refuge Manager Howard, posted in the tower throughout the day and watching every wink of Josephine's eye through a spyglass, guessed that she could hear the chick trying to break out of the shell. But darkness fell and still nothing had emerged. They left reluctantly, hardly slept that night, and climbed the tower again before dawn the next day.

With the first light of day they saw that both birds were standing by the nest, intent on whatever was hidden within its center. The two men waited all day, in almost unbearable impatience, and still no chick appeared, yet from the intentness of the parents Allen was convinced that there was a live infant crane within the grassy walls of the nest.

Later Allen wrote: "The following day, May 26, at a few minutes past six thirty in the morning I saw him. He was so tiny I could scarcely believe my eyes, but there he was, a rusty-colored downy little thing, moving about on the nest on his wobbly legs."

The news that for the first time in history a whooping crane had been hatched in captivity was on the air and on the front pages of newspapers here and abroad. For that moment at least, literally millions of people were poised over the bassinet of the baby crane and no doubt wishing it happiness and long life. Dr. Cottam, who flew to Texas from Washington, still recalls that it was a deeply thrilling moment when he got off the plane at Corpus Christi and picked up a newspaper with a full eight-column headline: WHOOPING CRANE IS BORN! Farther down in the paper he noticed a small item announcing the birth of a royal child to a European queen. He laughed with satisfaction and then sent both clippings to his wife with a note saying, "At last things are in proper proportion."

On his third day the chick, named Rusty, left the nest. Allen wrote: "I saw Rusty run across his father's big feet, running with the tottering friskiness of all small precocial birds. Then he came trotting back again, between the towering columns of Crip's long legs, and stopping, he looked up. No doubt he was uttering the 'strange, piping whistle' that Bradshaw heard when he saw the young whooper on the last Saskatchewan nest. Then Crip bent over with a soft and graceful tenderness, and finding the tiny mouth with the tip of his great bill, fed him. In all my experience with birds, this was the most wonderful, and the most moving scene I ever witnessed."

That afternoon the parent cranes began to wander in search of food, the chick running at their feet. Since the chick was no more than six inches high, Allen and Howard, who had still hardly left the tower, lost sight of it in the foot-high grass. With some anxiety they noticed several raccoons running along the flats. Howard sent one of his men out with a rifle, but by then the raccoons had disappeared.

The next morning, the chick's fourth day, Allen mounted the tower at dawn. There was a cold, biting rain. The parent birds were by the nest, and one of them seemed to be brooding the chick. Then suddenly the brooding bird arose and both birds walked away from the nest. They walked rapidly and without looking down. Allen, filled with horrible foreboding, called Howard on the field telephone in the tower. When he arrived the two men entered the enclosure. Josephine and Crip, who before had been so vigilant, were indifferent to their entry. Allen and Howard searched the muddy grass for hours, but found no trace of the chick. The empty nest was soggy in the rain. A few shards of eggshell lay nearby. Everywhere in the mud were the tracks of raccoons, making the chick's fate quite clear.

Rusty's loss was not the only misfortune to befall the cranes that year. The wild cranes, too, were having a hard time. All during the winter strong, dry winds had blown over the flats day after day. Little rain fell. Lakes and ponds on the refuge became mere stagnant puddles or vanished entirely. Along the shore the vegetation was thin, and inland the grass was as yellow as straw. With food hard to get, the wild cranes dispersed over a wide area. They migrated early. When they returned in the autumn of 1950, it was to unbroken drought.

The first bird appeared on October 5. For some time thereafter Howard was able to find only twenty birds. Then, searching by plane, he located twenty-eight. There were five young, of which two were twins. Still hoping to find more cranes, perhaps scattered by the abnormal weather, game agents were asked to search along the coast from the Sabine River to the Rio Grande, but they found nothing. The count of birds on the refuge remained uncertain because of the way they moved about, but after a great deal of figuring Howard decided to put down the official figure of twenty-six adults and four young. It appeared that seven cranes had perished in summer and that sometime in early January one of the twins had disappeared from the refuge. Its carcass was not found. Possibly it graced the dining table of some passing tugboat.

Howard's report for the last months of 1950 makes this seem the likeliest explanation, since he notes that "more than once" he saw shooting from boats but that they were too far away for him to identify their numbers and that without a boat of his own, pursuit was impossible. He also turned back several fishermen who came ashore on the refuge, and reprimanded two boys caught driving around the refuge with a gun and a dead goose—shot elsewhere, he believed—in their car.

As the drought continued in the winter of 1950–1951, it became the longest dry spell on record. Besides lack of rain there were abnormally low tides. Tidal pools were drained and cracked. It was possible to drive a jeep in areas that usually were too soft even for walking. To provide drinking water for the waterfowl, turkey, and deer, Howard used a dragline to excavate potholes in the dry lake beds. The cranes found the small puddles that remained on their territories too salty, and came inland to drink. One family came daily to a pothole dug in one of the lakes. They made an odd picture as they climbed out of the hole. Because of the low tides Josephine and Crip were able to leave their enclosure at will by walking around a fence that had once extended into deep water. Usually they did not wander far, and returned daily. Sometimes, when they lingered too long, Howard would go for them, rattling corn in a bucket, and they would quickly accompany him home to their enclosure.

The year 1950 was black not only for cranes but also for friends of cranes. In October, 1950, Robert Allen left the annual meeting of the American Ornithologists' Union, in Minneapolis, literally writhing with pain in his back. For months before this he had suffered a malaise that had been diagnosed as the result of a slipped disk. A doctor had put an uncomfortable cast on his neck which Allen had removed the first time he wanted to turn his head to count whooping cranes from an airplane. But this new pain could not be ignored. He got home to Florida and was given the grim diagnosis that he suffered from a form of progressive arthritis. He was told that the prognosis was unremitting pain, while his back stiffened, until he became immobile. After some months of contemplating such a future he was rescued by the then brand-new drug cortisone. Its effects were so beneficial that in a month he was able to get up and shortly was tramping through southern swamps searching for ivory-billed woodpeckers. In May, 1951, six months after the acute attack, he was able to make a strenuous trip to the Bahamas to study the nesting grounds of flamingos—a species whose troubles were next on the National Audubon Society's—and Allen's—agenda.

To prepare for a second season's nesting by Josephine and Crip, Allen designed a new pen, carefully planned to keep out predators. The original 150-acre tract was reduced to a rectangle a quarter of a mile long and a hundred yards wide, which included salt flats, shell ridges, and a portion of cattail marsh. An inner rearing pen, a hundred yards square, was built in the center with the thought that the parents and young could be herded into it when the young had hatched. As a further precaution the raccoons in the vicinity were done away with. On the advice of Fred Stark, of the San Antonio Zoo, Josephine and Crip were fed an enriched diet of yellow corn, chicken laying pellets, shrimp, ground horse meat, hardboiled eggs, and wheat-germ oil.

April passed, but though the captives danced they did not nest. Then, on May 12, 1951, Howard discovered a nest containing one egg on a small peninsula that extended into a tidal slough. The happy news was relayed to Washington, New York, and Florida.

Two days later a strong, steady east wind brought in the tide, and water crept to the edges of the nest. As the water rose the birds abandoned their incubating and both worked, in an anxious fashion, building up the nest. With growing dismay Howard saw that they were fighting a losing battle against the rising water. Nevertheless he was reluctant to interfere. Finally, at nine thirty that night, when it was obvious that only drastic action could save the egg, he waded out to the nest.

An overcast dimmed the moonlight, but he could see the white shapes of the cranes. He found the nest almost submerged. The egg was a quarter of an inch above the water, and cold droplets were splashing upon it. He withdrew and with his helpers brought armloads of dry hay and salt grass. They managed to lift the egg and nest together, so that the egg was untouched by their hands, and put a platform of hay under the nest. By now the nest site was an island with only the tops of the salt grass above the water. The wind was still blowing with gusts of thirty and forty miles an hour. Josephine and Crip, who did not attack, but bugled furiously, were dim white forms against the black water. The work of building up the nest took the men ten minutes. Then Howard climbed the tower and waited. At last, two hours later, one of the birds returned to the nest and began to brood. Relieved, Howard went to bed.

The next morning he could see that the reinforced nest had indeed weathered the storm, but instead of incubating the egg both birds were standing by the nest, probing at it in a peculiar fashion. Howard waded out and found that though the nest was sound and dry, the egg had disappeared. After a brief search, he found it smashed and floating amid the reeds. It seemed likely that the cranes had tried to rearrange the nest, causing the egg to roll out of its shallow resting place, and broken it as they attempted to push it back in place.

Although birds often nest a second time after such a loss, Josephine and Crip did not.

While these events were taking their course, twenty-nine wild cranes had migrated from the drought-stricken flats, leaving one bird behind. In September, 1951, Howard found its carcass, a month dead, on the refuge. Its major bones were unbroken, so it may have been that old age or illness prevented its migration and eventually killed it. The first migrants did not return until November, a little later than usual. One of the first to come in was obviously crippled. On November 12 a state employee found it on the ground near a windmill, unable to fly or stand, and brought it to headquarters. One leg had been shattered by gunshot. It had been hobbling on the injured leg until it grew too weak. Howard fed it corn and water and took it to San Antonio for care by Fred Stark, but it died shortly. A month later Howard found a whooping crane's corpse. This bird had lost a foot and had a break in the leg bone. It, too, had probably starved to death.

Compounding these losses was the fact that the summer toll had been terrible. Eight birds had been lost. This more than canceled the addition of five young that the survivors managed to bring back. The flock was back to a mere twenty-five. The death of eleven birds—one third of the flock—in a single year had wiped out all the gains of the past ten years.

It was at this point, when the fortunes of both wild and captive cranes were at a low ebb that George Douglass grew tired of waiting in the wings and stepped to center stage to play a decisive role in the future of the species. He demanded the return of "his" bird, Josephine.

Fate could not have selected a character more incongruous as custodian of what was now undoubtedly the single most valuable feathered creature in the world. Douglass was a politician by profession and a zookeeper by accident. He had been born in New Orleans in 1905. His father was an engineer who worked for the city and became a member of the Water Board. As a youth Douglass studied both accounting and law at Loyola University, but left without a degree to join his father in the Department of Waterworks. He worked in the personnel and accounting departments for five or six years, eventually becoming supervisor of several departments. In 1941 the director of Audubon Park died. A replacement was sought, and Douglass applied for the job. The Board of Commissioners of Audubon Park—twenty-four local civic leaders who are appointed by the mayor—did not feel that Douglass's inexperience in zoological matters was any hindrance to his appointment, since running the zoo was considered mainly an administrative job, and in any case merely one segment of Park Department affairs.

Douglass's qualifications included membership in the business and political fraternity of the city. He was personable, friendly, a natty dresser, and popular at businessmen's luncheons. As director of the zoo, then, Douglass's single drawback was that he knew very little about animals. Even this wouldn't have mattered much in the course of world affairs had not fate made Josephine—the only captive, female whooping crane on earth—his charge.

Until the moment Josephine began to lay her golden eggs no one had given any thought to the question of her ownership. Was she a gift or a loan to the zoo? Since wild migratory birds are under federal protection, had anyone the right to give her to anyone else? After ten years the circumstances of her arrival at the zoo were undocumented and confused. There was no written record beyond the file card in the zoo's office. The state and federal game wardens who brought the bird to the zoo had not bothered to inform anyone else of the incident, so, until

Robert Allen conceived the idea of breeding Josephine and Pete, Washington officials of the Fish and Wildlife Service not only didn't care who had custody of Josephine; they hadn't known she existed.

There is no truer truism than that possession is nine tenths of the law. During the negotiations that preceded bringing Crip and Josephine together, not only common sense but common courtesy prompted all concerned to request the "permission" of Douglass—and the Audubon Park Board—for the "loan" of "the Park's" bird. John Baker had given assurance that if the experiment were a "failure," Josephine would be returned. What, exactly, constituted failure had, of course, not been defined.

In any case, late in 1951, Douglass came to his own decision that the breeding experiment was a failure and that it was his duty to demand that she once again ornament the New Orleans Zoo. He expressed this line of thought to the local newspapers, with the result that his and Josephine's name appeared in large type. The Texas newspapers were quick to take up the issue, arguing against her removal from Aransas. From this evolved a state's-rights editorial battle that amused everyone except the few people—like Robert Allen—who viewed Josephine, not as a tourist attraction, but as the final, fragile possessor of genes that no power on earth could duplicate.

On December 13, 1951, Douglass made a sudden move that apparently caught the United States Fish and Wildlife Service off balance. He got into the zoo's panel truck, drove to Aransas, strode into the office of manager Julian Howard, and told him, "I've come to get my bird." Howard asked him to wait while he telephoned Washington. That day Dr. Cottam was Acting Director in the absence of Director Albert M. Day, and received the call. As Dr. Cottam now recalls the events of that day, he was both taken by surprise, and appalled. He had been interested in the cranes since the early days of Aransas. Now that captive breeding had come within an ace of success, he was deeply anxious to have the effort continue. Furthermore, he did not feel that Douglass's accidental possession of Josephine had made the bird his private property, or that of the Audubon Zoo.

In legal matters the United States Fish and Wildlife Service is counseled by the Office of the Solicitor of the Department of the Interior. Douglass's claim on Josephine was clearly a matter for legal decision. Cottam told Julian Howard to keep Douglass waiting, and on no account to surrender Josephine, while he consulted the department's lawyers. He has described what happened next as "just another one of those unfortunate things that dogs the cranes." According to Dr. Cottam the lawyer into whose hands the question happened to fall was a man who saw no importance in a problem involving a single bird. He shortly delivered the opinion that Josephine should be returned to Douglass.

Dr. Cottam was, in his own words, "fit to be tied." He determined to take the question up another rung of the ladder, to the head of the Legal Department. A second call from Howard at Aransas saying that Douglass was now threatening to take Josephine by force did not help Dr. Cottam keep cool. To the misfortune of the cranes, the lawyer who had ruled in Douglass's favor had already reached his superior and recited the story. Dr. Cottam is still convinced that had the issue been differently presented at this time the outcome would have been different. As it was, the chief solicitor backed the opinion of his subordinate, and ruled that the service must relinquish Josephine. Dr. Cottam had no further recourse. He telephoned Aransas and told Howard to surrender her. Then, on the slim hope that Josephine and Crip would breed at New Orleans, Cottam offered to allow Douglass to take Crip as well, provided Douglass would sign a release acknowledging the government's ownership of Crip. "They were a mated pair and I felt it would be criminal to separate them," Cottam has since said. "But I was so damn mad and rattled that I didn't think to put in a clause covering ownership of their offspring. Don't think I don't kick myself for that."

Victoriously, Douglass bore off his two prizes. At the zoo he put them on exhibit in a cage ten feet square.

Once the transfer of Josephine and Crip had become a *fait accompli* the losers elected to bow to defeat gracefully. A news release was issued from Aransas blandly stating: "After a visit since the fall of 1948, Josephine . . . is leaving Aransas for her home state. She has been on loan from the Audubon Park Commission to the Fish and Wildlife Service in their efforts to perpetuate the species. . . . The U.S. Fish and Wildlife Service has agreed to loan Crip for one breeding season or until another mate for him is secured. . . ."

John Baker, too, felt that nothing would be gained by further public airing of the affair. The next issue of *Audubon Magazine* ran a story that reviewed how the Audubon Park Zoo had "generously loaned" Josephine to the Fish and Wildlife Service and the National Audubon Society for three nesting seasons. It went on: "When the Audubon Park Commission recently indicated that, in view of the circumstances, it would like to be given the opportunity to demonstrate whether it could succeed . . . in raising young whooping cranes at a zoo, for later liberation in the wild, it was felt by the Fish and Wildlife Service and your Society that the request was a reasonable one, even though we both believe it would be preferable to continue the breeding experiment under as natural conditions as possible, and that the chances of young cranes surviving in the wild, after being raised in a zoo, are slight. It was felt . . . the captive adults should stay together and so decision was made to offer to loan the male to the Commission for ten months . . . as well as return the female. This decision was . . . disheartening to the Refuge Manager, who had done so much to give the captives all possible aid and who had become very much attached to them. . . . While the incident caused considerable publicity in Texas and Louisiana papers, with expressions of rival claims as to jurisdiction, and involvement of the issue of state's rights, all was in good humor!"

This was the first, but by no means the last, time that the circumstances of Josephine's residence at New Orleans were politely withheld from public discussion.

12

In early 1952, Robert Allen's monograph *The Whooping Crane* was published by the National Audubon Society. It was a massive piece of work, analyzing in painstaking detail all the information, both historical and current, that he had been able to gather about whooping cranes and their environment. Since the entire purpose of the study was to provide the Fish and Wildlife Service with practical information to be used in providing help for the cranes, the most important sections of the monograph were those labeled "Survival: Protection and Conservation."

Leading Allen's list of recommendations were those concerned with the food supply at Aransas, the reasons for the periodic failure of marine life along its shores, and steps that could be taken to prevent dearth of food and water from driving the cranes into alien territory. He noted that an alert manager at Aransas could foretell winter food scarcity, and act accordingly. Certain bayous might be equipped with tide gates so that marine food animals could be stocked. Inland ponds could be dug and stocked with killifish, frogs, and crayfish. "We feed game birds in winter," he wrote, "why not whooping cranes?"

The report discussed means of protecting the cranes from shooting and disturbance at Aransas. It named those areas of the bay, the Waterway, and adjacent islands that should be more adequately protected. "Constant patrol by a deeply interested and able warden would do immeasurable good," Allen wrote. He suggested that the boundaries of the area closed to shooting should be enlarged so that it would no longer be legal to shoot ducks from blinds within two hundred yards of the cranes' territory and that an effort should be made to persuade the State of Texas to close Mustang Lake to fishermen. Ideally, the lake should be added to the refuge, as should every other available inch of whooper habitat, for as things stood, if the population of cranes increased, the shortage of habitat would become critical.

Allen took up the threat of oil pollution, pointing out that if a quantity of oil were accidentally spilled from rigs working in the bay it could be fatal to the whooping cranes. Meanwhile, the disturbing effects of drilling on the refuge could be kept at a minimum only by continued cooperation from the oil companies concerned.

Harassment by low-flying aircraft that might drive the whoopers from the refuge was a similar problem. As a practical matter, the refuge manager dealt with it by informally asking the local commanding officers to caution their pilots; but, Allen suggested, it would be better if an official ceiling could be established, as well as a definite arrangement with the Armed Services to safeguard whooping-crane territories on Matagorda and St. Joseph islands.

Allen also felt that more could be done for the cranes to guard them on their migration route: "The Platte River has long been a major stopping place for the whooper migrants, yet no safe resting place has been provided for them. A Federal refuge for waterfowl and whooping cranes should be established along no less than fifty miles of the Platte River in Nebraska." In addition he urged the importance of continual effort to reach hunters along the cranes' route by all possible means of publicity.

Although Allen's monograph was primarily a scientific document, he was never entirely successful in preventing his passionate feelings about the cranes from cropping up among his dispassionately presented facts; as when he wrote:

"When you sit crouched in a blind and watch an adult Whooper stride close by you, his head high and proud, his bearing arrogant and imposing, you feel the presence of a strength and of a stubborn will to survive that is one of the vital intangibles of this entire situation. Certainly it cannot be overlooked. We have a strong conviction that the Whooping Crane will keep his part of the bargain and will fight for survival every inch of the way. What are we going to do to help? Here, in this report, is the challenge, here is the job that must be done."

To underscore Allen's warnings on dangers to the cranes, Howard's reports to Washington reflected increasingly hectic activity at Aransas. During 1951, oil wells 19 and 20 had been drilled. Increased production prompted Continental Oil and its sublessee, Western Natural Gas, to plan a new barge-loading dock requiring a pipeline and road laid directly across whooping-crane territory. They were finally persuaded to choose another route—at some financial sacrifice. For this forbearance the National Audubon Society presented them with a Citation of Merit.

A total of 3,422 visitors registered at headquarters during 1951, and it was Manager Howard's belief that most of them came in the hope of glimpsing, from the tower, the distant white forms of whooping cranes. Not counted as "visitors" were the fifty or more people who came to the refuge daily to tend the cattle and to work on the oil company's fast developing installations on the interior of the refuge. The road traffic

"When you watch a whooper stride by," Allen wrote, "his head high and proud . . . you feel a strength . . . and a stubborn will to survive."

to the oil sites became very heavy: "a continuous stream day and night," Howard wrote.

In the autumn of 1951 the refuge was plagued by a rash of hunting violations. One of them involved a man from Rosenberg, Texas, who, as Howard put it, "takes the furlined bathtub for the blunder of the year." After registering at headquarters the man drove half a mile south and blazed away at some ducks in a roadside pond, believing, he said, that this was a public hunting area. The bathtub winner was stopped before he hit any ducks, and later fined $100 in a state court.

In early December, Howard caught a man shooting from a boat on the Waterway, and the next day nabbed two more shooting on the refuge itself. In the course of an air survey to count whooping cranes, Howard discovered a man and his wife who had been squatting for a month at a pleasant spot within whooping-crane territory known as Cape Carlos. They were allowed three days to pack and leave.

In the early months of 1952 there was some rain, but because the thirsty sands soaked it up like a blotter, the drought was not entirely ended. Owing to a shortage of food on the marshes, the cranes "continued to feed within easy slingshot range of the canal." This, Howard noted, "constitutes a hazard to the wintering population."

On March 20, 1952, around midnight, Howard was awakened by gunfire. He leaped from bed in his pajamas and arrested three men who had shot a doe directly in front of headquarters.

That spring Howard was unsure of the number of whooping cranes on the refuge. He reported that at least twenty-five migrants had returned from Canada, with twenty-three surviving the winter, but it was possible that two more had gone uncounted. Several single cranes that moved restlessly about caused the confusion. Whether twenty-five or twenty-three, the last of the migrant cranes left Aransas at the end of April. Howard saw the final pair flying in a circle and calling to each other, then drifting up and away until they vanished in the sky.

During the summer there was constant drilling in San Antonio and St. Charles bays. Howard reported: "It is apparent we are entering a period of rapid and intensified exploration for gas and oil. Despite cooperative efforts to reduce damage and disturbance to water fowl areas, it is visualized as an uphill struggle between the dollar and the duck."

In the autumn of 1952 there were rains in the northern part of the state, but the showers missed Aransas and, as waterfowl and whooping cranes returned, the shortage of drinking water was critical. Only nineteen adult and two young whooping cranes reached the refuge. Of the six (or eight) adults that had been lost over the summer, the fate of one became known. On October 31, children near Olathe, Kansas, found a wounded whooping crane in a cornfield and brought it to school. A game warden drove all night in an attempt to get it to the San Antonio Zoo, but it died on the way.

A few days later game agents in Regina, Saskatchewan, telegraphed to Washington: "Have a live, injured whooping crane. Immature. Wing tip off. Knee badly damaged. Will try to force-feed." Washington dispatched a plane to get the bird, but it, too, died en route.

Audubon Magazine commented, "Each year it becomes more apparent that illegal hunting is the major factor in reducing the numbers of the whooping cranes."

In the spring of 1952, when Josephine and Crip should have been nesting, Dr. Cottam visited them at Audubon Park. He found them on exhibit in their ten-foot coop. Mustering all his self-control, Dr. Cottam explained gently to Douglass that whooping cranes require both solitude and large premises in order to nest. Dr. Cottam's effort was rewarded: some time later, when John Baker also visited the two captives, he found that their enclosure had indeed been enlarged and moved behind the elephant house, where it was out of the way of heavy traffic. Having decided to keep smiling in public, Baker made no published comment on any shortcomings he may have noticed, but wrote in *Audubon Magazine* that he had found the birds "in fine condition," in a special enclosure three hundred feet square.

Josephine and Crip evidently felt differently about things, for they did not nest, either that spring or the next.

During 1953, John Baker, distressed at the plight of Josephine and Crip, and the waste of their valuable potential, cast about for a means to rescue the birds. At length he hatched a plan to persuade Douglass to "lend" the birds to the National Audubon Society's Rainey Sanctuary, a large and secluded tract in southwestern Louisiana.

Baker entered into tactful correspondence with Douglass, pointing out that to all who truly cared about the preservation of the species the furtherance of a successful nesting by Josephine and Crip overrode all other considerations and that quite possibly the semiwild habitat at the Rainey Sanctuary would be more conducive to success than the necessarily unnatural conditions of the zoo. Douglass replied smoothly that of course, his greatest concern was for the safety of the two precious birds. Therefore, a decision of such importance as their transfer to Rainey Sanctuary must rest, not with him, but with the New Orleans Park Board.

On January 4, 1954, Baker again wrote Douglass a cordial note expressing surprise that he had heard nothing further about the plan to move the captive whooping cranes to the Rainey Sanctuary in time for a possible nesting that spring. Douglass answered that the question of transferring the whooping cranes to the sanctuary had been discussed at the Park Board meeting in December and laid over until the next meeting on January 27. He wished Baker a very happy New Year.

Just prior to this January 27 meeting of the twenty-four New Orleans civic gentlemen who now, curiously, were being called upon to make a decision that might settle for all time the fate of *Grus americana,* John Baker again wrote to Douglass: "Dear George . . . I had hoped you would have visited the Rainey Sanctuary to determine to your satisfaction that the transfer would be practical."

On January 28, the day after the meeting, Douglass replied to "Dear John" that several members of the Board were acquainted with the location of the Sanctuary and that none of them thought well of the idea. He went on to say that the Rainey Sanctuary lacked blue crabs, knowledgeably quoting Robert Allen on "blue crabs as a principal item of whooping crane diet." He closed by mentioning a fear of predators, which could hardly have been an unintentional reminder of the death of Rusty. John Baker remained unruffled on paper. "Dear George," he wrote, "I am rather surprised that several members of your board do not think well . . ." He politely pointed out that the Rainey Sanctuary was in an area that once supported many wild whoopers and that the National Society planned to build a vermin-proof enclosure a hundred acres in extent that would be patrolled by a full-time warden. Here, for the moment, the correspondence rested.

The zoological world is bigger than the average sewing circle; nevertheless, news gets around it fast. By this time a good many ornithologists, related scientists, and bird lovers had become interested in whooping cranes, and were by no means generally satisfied to have Josephine and Crip remain at the New Orleans Zoo. One of those who felt most deeply dissatisfied was Dr. S. Dillon Ripley, 2nd, who at that time was Curator of Vertebrate Zoology of the Peabody Museum at Yale, and is now Secretary of the Smithsonian Institution in Washington. The situation of the whoopers had caught Dr. Ripley's eye for two reasons. He is a vigorous member of several international organizations for the preservation of endangered species, and his hobby, to which he is ardently devoted, is breeding waterfowl in captivity. When, by the end of June, 1954, it was clear that the captive whoopers at New Orleans had let another season go by without breeding, Dr. Ripley decided to see what he could do about it. He wrote a long letter to a number of men who were, in various ways, influential in wildlife conservation, describing the sorry situation of the species *Grus americana*, both captive and free, and urging that some way be found to provide Josephine and Crip with skilled avicultural care.

Rearing captive cranes, Dr. Ripley wrote, might turn out to be the basic factor in saving the species. "There is now in existence a known, proven, breeding pair of captive cranes . . . these cranes will breed again, given proper supervision and care. The nub of this entire problem lies in the proper supervision and care. . . . Technicians of this sort are unfortunately rare in the United States. . . . There are not more than two or three men in the USA who could be entrusted with such precious charges, or such a weighty assignment. However, in the meantime I for one consider it a criminally irresponsible thing to *waste* the present proven breeding pair, to eke out their meager and barren lives in the Audubon Zoo in New Orleans. The chance of their breeding further is simply being thrown away, and the Audubon Zoo should be encouraged to realize this and to cooperate to the full to save the species. . . ."

This letter proved to be something like a large rock thrown into a small pond; the ensuing waves hit the shore in all directions, and were to surge back and forth for the next ten years.

One of the first ripples evidently reached George Douglass at New Orleans, who thereafter became noticeably touchy on the subject of captive whooping cranes. Some months later he found means to take a countermeasure when the zoo was visited by French-born Jean Delacour, an ornithologist of renown, who became an American citizen and who was then curator of the Los Angeles County Museum.

After a tour of the zoo and a pleasant dinner, Douglass elicited from Delacour a testimonial to the quality of the zoo's care of the cranes. Under the date November 17, 1954, Delacour wrote, in part: "In the company of Dr. George Lowery of the University of Louisiana, Baton Rouge, I went to the New Orleans Zoo to see a pair of captive whooping cranes in that establishment. I found the accommodation was very good. It is large and secluded enough, and well protected against any possible predators. The food given the birds, consisting of laying pellets, corn, crabs and shrimp, seems to be excellent. . . . I see no reason why they should not breed in this pen. . . . I would recommend therefore, that the birds be left at the New Orleans zoo under the present conditions and it is very likely that now that they have settled down completely in their new pen, they will start breeding." For the next ten years Douglass kept a supply of mimeographed copies of this curious document in a desk drawer at the zoo, ready to hand out to visitors.

Meanwhile John Baker had not yet relinquished his hope of getting the captive cranes moved to the Rainey Sanctuary. When Douglass sent him a copy of Delacour's report, Baker replied with thanks, and again mentioned the Rainey Sanctuary project. Douglass did not reply. On May 26, 1955, Baker wrote again. "Dear George . . . Not having heard from you about any nesting of the captive whoopers this spring I rather assume they again failed to lay . . . time is marching on and I hope you will feel as I do that some new efforts should be made to obtain young from the captive birds. . . . You have had the birds for three years: the Aransas Refuge had them for three years before that, and I think you know I feel there would be a better attitude on the part of some of our ornithological friends if an arrangement could be worked out whereby someone . . . known to have had successful experience . . . were given an opportunity to show what . . . he could obtain at a new location."

Douglass's reply a week later was a shock. He wrote to "Dear John" that on Sunday, May 29, he had found an egg in a nest of straw in the whooping crane yard. The egg was discovered at 7 A.M. and at 10:30 it was found to be broken. He had hopes that another would be laid. In regard to Baker's letter, he did not feel any new effort should be made to obtain young from the captive birds. He felt he was doing well enough at it was. He further remarked that in regard to Baker's statement that there "would be a better attitude, etc." that this was out of order.

Thus, at the very moment when, after so much disappointment there again seemed to be hope of breeding captive cranes, and when, therefore, skilled handling would be most crucial, Douglass had slammed the door on Baker and, it seemed, on any project to move the captives. John Baker's feelings at this juncture may well be imagined. However, he sent back a soft answer. His letter disclaimed responsibility for any hostile remarks about Douglass, and closed with the whisper: "You seem to be having somewhat the same kind of heartbreaking difficulties that were experienced at Aransas."

Douglass did not notify Baker of the particular heartbreaking difficulty he experienced when Josephine laid a second egg. Douglass, delighted, allowed reporters and photographers to view the historic scene. In the course of the hustle and bustle of newcomers around the nesting pen, someone took it into his head to tease the whooping cranes by poking a stick through the wire. Crip became so furious in defense of the nest that he accidentally stepped on the egg and smashed it. Josephine laid no more eggs that year.

13

After Allen's two unsuccessful searches for the cranes' nesting grounds, ending in 1948, there were no further organized efforts, although each summer Fish and Wildlife biologists making their regular rounds to count waterfowl kept on the lookout for whoopers. For three summers no new clues showed up; then, suddenly, Robert Smith, the biologist with whom Allen had flown, sighted two whooping cranes in a remote area north of Great Slave Lake. On July 15, 1952, he wrote to Allen: "Two of the elusive great white birds found north of Great Slave Lake—just north of Deep Bay. The first one was found July 11 and the next day we went back and saw it again. . . . We then found another one about 30 miles away. The way they act there might be nests nearby. . . . It is not possible to land anywhere near the birds and it would be quite a project to get to them on foot. . . . You and I flew over the same area twice, once in '47 and again in '48 and from my experience the other day they could have been there then. It took us 20 minutes to locate the first one a second time and we knew almost exactly where he was."

This was tantalizing news but difficult to follow up. Baker and Allen decided to postpone a search on the ground until there had been further reconnoitering by air. In August, Smith flew over the region again, but this time found nothing, so further search was put off for another year.

In early June, 1953, Smith again surveyed the area, and drew a blank. Then, on June 21, a Canadian helicopter pilot reported encountering a huge white bird in the air close to the spot at which Smith had seen the two whoopers the previous summer. Finally, in October, W. Winston Mair, then Chief of the Canadian Wildlife Service, telegraphed Washington: "Eight whoopers reliably reported south bound along Slave River October 6."

Thus, as the summer of 1953 ended, although no whooping-crane nests had been seen, there was reason to hope that soon, perhaps in one more season, the mystery of the nesting grounds would be unlocked at last.

While this was exciting and hopeful news, there was nothing cheering in the situation as it had developed at Aransas during the past year and a half. In the autumn of 1952 there were only twenty-one wild whoopers.

The following summer, thanks perhaps to a massive publicity campaign in which the Audubon Society, the State Fish and Game departments, and the Canadian and United States Wildlife Services all cooperated, the flock made the round trip without losing a single adult bird. Nesting, however, was less successful, or possibly the young perished en route south. In any case only three young were added, and so the flock numbered twenty-four in the autumn of 1953—a precarious figure, to say the least.

There had been few improvements at Aransas to brighten the picture. Nature had helped somewhat, for the drought broke in 1953, but otherwise matters were much as before. The refuge now possessed a boat, but there was no regular patrol of the Waterway or the marshes to guard against poachers, and no supplementary feeding, so that whenever their food supplies deteriorated some of the whooping cranes moved off the refuge.

In April, 1954, when the twenty-four cranes left Texas, the society and the two Wildlife services agreed to launch a ground expedition to search for the nests as soon as there were any new reports of cranes sighted in Canada. May and June passed without news, and then the Canadian Wildlife Service dispatched from Ottawa what Allen called "an electrifying message." Dated July 2, 1954, it read: "Dear Mr. Baker, We have just received a telegram from W. A. Fuller, our mammologist at Fort Smith, Northwest Territories, stating that four or possibly six whooping cranes were seen from a helicopter in Wood Buffalo Park, NWT, on June 30th. The group included a pair with one young. . . . We expect more details next week."

The details came in a letter from William Fuller. The discovery, he wrote, had been due to the sheerest accident. On June 30 a fire had broken out in a remote section of Wood Buffalo Park, which because of its forbidding terrain is one of the least known regions of Canada. A helicopter belonging to the Canadian Forest Service was dispatched from Fort Smith, at the northeast corner of the park.

Aboard the helicopter were the pilot, Don Landells, and G. M. Wilson, Superintendent of Forestry. On the return trip from the fire they flew low over a swampy region near the Sass River. Both men chanced to look down, and there, standing tall, and gleaming white against the dark terrain, were two birds that Wilson was certain were whooping cranes. Most marvelous of all, he could clearly see beside them a long-legged, rusty little bird, about the size of a large rooster—obviously a whooping-crane fledgling. He radioed the discovery to Fort Smith.

That same evening the helicopter set out again, this time with William Fuller aboard. As they circled the area that Landells had marked on his map, Fuller spotted two whooping cranes. There was no doubt of the

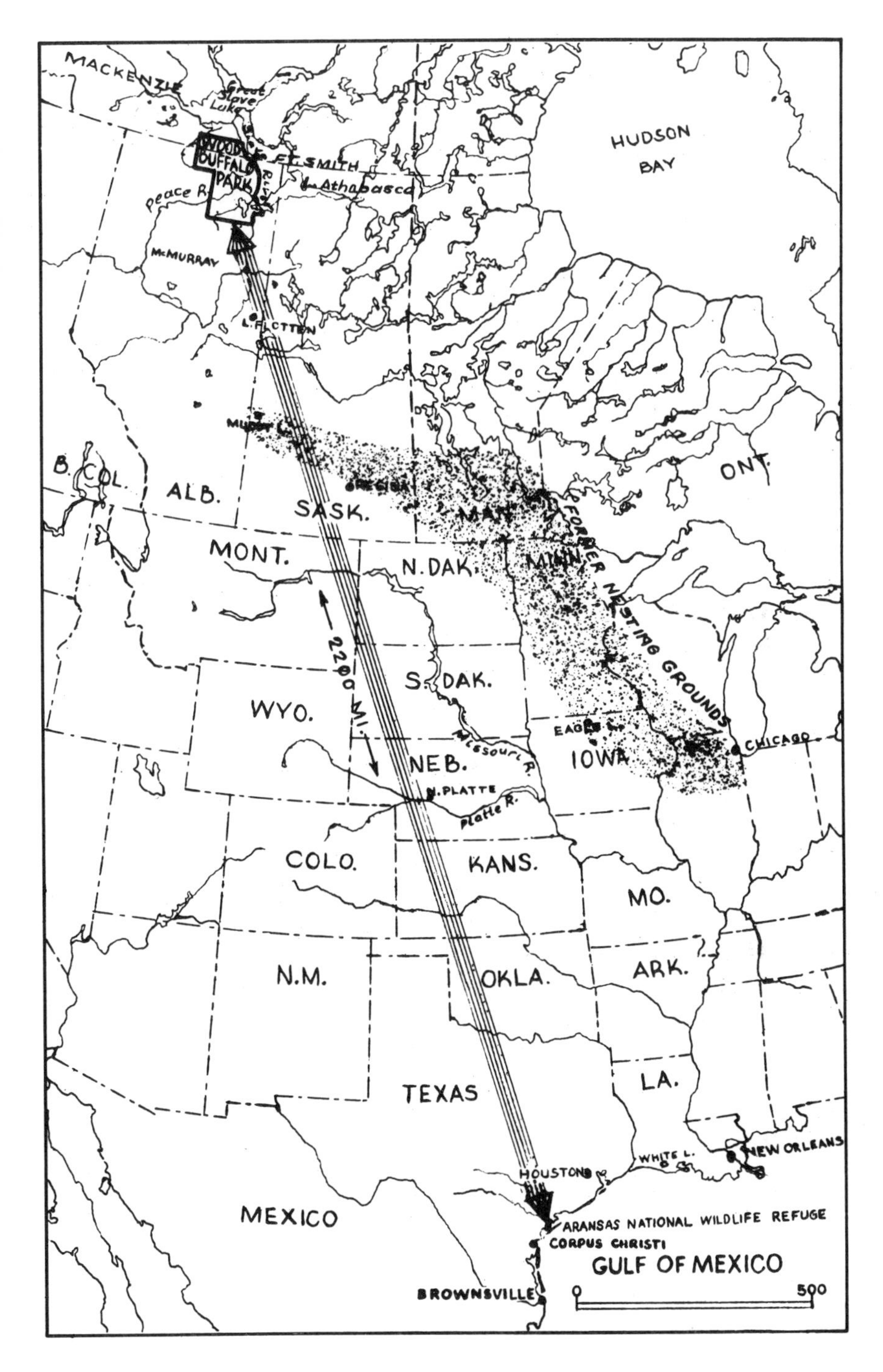

Whooping Crane Nesting Grounds

identification—he could see the vivid red crowning their heads. The only question was whether this was a second pair or the original pair with the young bird now out of sight. Finally, as a sort of dividend, they saw yet another whooper, a single, near the Nyarling River, some miles to the northwest.

Fuller had wanted to land near the cranes, but the terrain was too formidable. It was, he reported, an area dotted with small, shallow, muddy lakes separated by narrow zones of spiky black spruce. Ground travel appeared to be nearly impossible. Fuller guessed that the only access would be the twisting course of the Sass River.

John Baker telephoned the news to Allen, who was in Florida. That evening Allen wrote to him, "Our telephone conversation this afternoon . . . has been, for me, like the clanging of a bell to an old fire horse!" However, he added regretfully, he felt it was too late to undertake an expedition that season.

The Canadian authorities agreed, but promised to keep tabs on the area by helicopter and protect the nests by banning unauthorized aircraft from that section of the park. As an added precaution the exact location of the nests was kept as nearly secret as possible. On this point Baker felt strongly. "Our experience leads us to recommend extreme caution," he wrote. "There are individuals who will go to almost any length to get a specimen of a species . . . threatened with extinction."

In this instance Baker need not have worried. The spot the whooping cranes had chosen was almost literally impenetrable in summer, and this, of course, was why the nests had eluded observation for so long.

Wood Buffalo National Park covers 17,300 square miles—more than Massachusetts, Connecticut, Rhode Island, and Delaware combined. Once considered economically valueless, it had been set aside in 1922 as a preserve for the last of Canada's herds of wild bison. The cranes' nest ground in the northeast corner of the park, although only a hundred miles west of Fort Smith as the crane flies, might as well have been in the center of the Land of Oz, since it was cut off by natural barriers so formidable that it had been virtually unexplored. Airplanes usually avoided flying over it because it offered no landing places in case of emergency; its lakes were too shallow for pontoon planes and the muskeg too soft for conventional aircraft. Its rivers were so choked by fallen timber as to be practically unnavigable. Thus it is likely that very few men, white or Indian, had ever set foot within the cranes' enclave.

In the autumn of 1954, the return of the cranes to Aransas was awaited with more than usual eagerness. In September, Howard began daily trips to the marsh. At 10:00 A.M. on October 17, his assistant, Everett Beaty, saw three adults fly into Mustang Lake. Their weary behavior made him think that he had seen an actual arrival for the first time.

Two more pairs appeared that afternoon. Gradually the population built up until there were twenty-one adults on the refuge. But the little bird that had been seen in Canada never got through. For the first time since records had been kept, all the young of that summer somehow perished. Three adults had also been lost. Howard reported to Washington: "With a drop of three, and no young, the situation becomes ever more critical."

The fact that no young had arrived at Aransas made Allen feel that it was more than ever vital to explore the breeding ground. He hoped to determine whether the nests, or the young whooping cranes, were being destroyed there, perhaps by storms or by predators, or whether the losses were, as he suspected, the result of shooting on the flyway. In November, Allen went to Ottawa to see Winston Mair, Chief of the Canadian Wildlife Service, and planned an expedition for the summer of 1955. He arranged that Fuller, at Fort Smith, would begin air surveys in early May; as soon as nesting cranes were sighted a ground party would try to reach the spot.

In April the whooping cranes began moving north from Aransas. On April 12 Julian Howard happened to be watching a pair at the moment they departed. As he wrote later: "A pair was located near the bay . . . we stopped to watch them. The weather was overcast with low clouds and a strong southeast wind. . . . After eight or ten minutes the pair extended their necks . . . two or three quick steps and they were airborne. With the high wind they quickly gained altitude and circled the first time at approximately 150 feet. As they continued circling they gained altitude and drifted with the wind. . . . In three or four minutes they were lost against the low gray clouds."

Eighteen days later, on April 30, a pair of whooping cranes, possibly this same pair, had covered the twenty-five hundred miles from Texas to Wood Buffalo Park. William Fuller wired to Mair that from the air he had sighted two birds on the Upper Sass River within a mile of the spot at which cranes had been seen the year before. In a memorandum he added: "The Sass River is navigable at the present stage of water (it is now open and flowing fast), although there may be some difficulty with beaver dams. . . . My recommendations would be for the ground party to commence operations as early as possible."

Meanwhile, Robert Allen, who had not expected such an early summons from the North, was in the Bahamas studying flamingos when John Baker radioed him to return immediately. He reached Fort Smith on May 20. Two days before, on another air survey, Fuller had seen a grand total of seven cranes, one of them near a nest in which he was even able to see an egg. The birds were all within an area of approximately five hundred square miles—a pocket handkerchief from the air, but an immensity on the ground. A few days after Allen arrived, he, too, flew over the nesting area: "There beneath us was the sight I had been hoping to see for almost ten years—a wild whooping crane on its nest! The incubating bird continued to sit as we flew by, circling at 1,000 feet. Its size and outline, even its posture, were unmistakable. I could see that it was turning to watch us as we passed, its head up and its yellow eye doubtless glaring at us with hostility and a total lack of fear."

The search party assembled by Allen consisted of himself, Ray Stewart, Fuller's assistant in place of Fuller, who was unable to go; and Bob Stewart of the United States Fish and Wildlife Service. From aerial photographs Allen had concluded that the best way to reach the Sass—the swift and narrow stream that twists through the heart of the nest area—was to travel some forty miles downstream on the Slave River to a spot known as the Grand Detour, and thence make a long portage overland to the Little Buffalo River. A few miles' travel upstream on the Little Buffalo would lead them into the Sass, which would, after many twists and turns, take them into whooping-crane country.

On May 23 the three explorers set forth on the Slave. With them were ten Indians who were to carry their five hundred pounds of equipment over the Grand Detour portage. The air was bright and cold. Ice on the riverbank glittered in the sun. At Grand Detour the overland trek began. Allen was relieved to find that his ailing back stood the strain of the heavy going. They traveled through damp spruce woods and then across marshy prairie to the shore of a slough connecting with the Little Buffalo River. There the Indians put down their loads and left them. The searchers were on their own. After a second day of hard going—on foot and by canoe—and another long, cold twilight night in camp, they reached the Sass River. Spirits high, they launched their canoe. Rounding the first bend, they found the river blocked by a mighty logjam. After a half hour of hacking they cut through it only to find a bigger jam just ahead. One of the men made his way through the brush along the river bank and reported that beyond the second jam was a third, beyond that a fourth, and so on, undoubtedly ad infinitum. The Sass River was hopelessly unnavigable, and the whoopers' nests as tantalizingly unreachable as ever. Four days later, after a difficult return trip, the party was once again at Fort Smith. It was as depressing a moment as Allen had faced in all his endeavors for the whooping cranes.

Defeated on the ground Allen now arranged to charter a commercial helicopter. On June 4 the party was in the air heading for a spot near the Sass where a distinctive limestone escarpment marked the vicinity of the cranes' nests. In due time the helicopter landed them in the wilderness, and departed. The men made camp and then began to hunt for the landmarks, shown on their aerial maps, that would lead them to the cranes. After four futile days of tramping in all directions, they realized the bitter truth: the helicopter had put them down near the wrong escarpment. For almost two weeks the party remained marooned in the wilderness while Forest Service officials at Fort Smith—whom they could reach by radio—tried to find a helicopter to rescue them. At length Fort Smith radioed that no helicopter could be procured, and recommended that they try to get out under their own steam. Their escape took five days of infinitely painful travel. One entire day was spent on the Sass River, hacking through forty logjams and three beaver dams in order to cover an airline distance of a mile and a half.

They reached Fort Smith, exhausted and defeated. Since it appeared impossible to charter a second helicopter, their expedition seemed at an end. Robert Stewart, the United States Fish and Wildlife man, left by plane immediately. Allen planned to stay on for a few days to tie up loose ends.

On the following day, Allen dropped into district headquarters to see Ward Stevens, Superintendent of Game, and found a message that a helicopter would be available two days hence. Weary as they were, Allen and Ray Stewart went back to work, repacking their battered equipment and compiling a grub list.

For this third attempt Stevens offered to transport the expedition in the service's riverboat to a rendezvous with the helicopter on the Slave River. A landing strip was created by lashing a large wooden platform to the bow of the boat. The party set off on the river in the rosy dusk of midnight and reached the rendezvous point by morning. At noon the helicopter appeared and settled neatly on the platform.

Later, Allen wrote John Baker as follows: "It was about 1:15 P.M. on June 23rd when we made our second try by helicopter. . . . We flew west until we saw the Little Buffalo and then, after a few anxious minutes, located the twists and turns of our Nemesis, the Sass. Soon we could make out the strange dark patches, three in number, that we had selected as our landmark. Studying them and their relative size and positions carefully we were certain, from their appearance on the aerial photographs, that this was the spot. . . . Holmgren [the pilot], without a moment's hesitation, landed exactly where we indicated. As soon as we were unloaded he took off for the second run, which would deliver the remainder of our gear.

"I wrote in my notes: 'It has taken us 31 days and a lot of grief, but let it be known that at 2 P.M., on this 23rd day of June, we are on the ground with the whooping cranes!' "

From the air Allen had seen a pretty green-and-brown pattern of ponds, lakes, and snaky streams, interwoven with patches of forest and brush. From the ground the terrain was more forbidding. They had landed close to the Sass, at the edge of an open area—a brûlé—burned over perhaps fifteen or twenty years before. Here and there the dark skeletons of spruce and tamarack stood naked and bereaved-looking. To the east the marshy banks of the river had stopped the fire, and beyond it were thickets of mixed brush and stunted trees that, Allen knew from their air survey, surrounded a bewildering network of shallow ponds. Amid those ponds and bogs and brush-covered ridges was the inner sanctum sheltering the nests of the whooping cranes. As so often happens in moments of final achievement, Allen and Stewart were unable to feel the high elation they had so long looked forward to—they were too weary and too oppressed by the grim inhospitality of the landscape. They made camp by the river—accompanied everywhere by the cus-

Whooping crane nest site, Sass River, Wood Buffalo National Park.

tomary cloud of mosquitoes—and settled down, wanting nothing more but sleep.

The next morning they set out to explore. Allen later wrote to John Baker: "The walking was difficult across the mushy surface of the burn, and once we had dropped into the pothole area to the west, it was even worse. Unexpectedly, the land between the ponds and tiny lakes is thickly grown with dwarf birch, willows, tamaracks and scraggly black spruce. Once in the middle of such a thicket one's vision is strictly limited. Often we were unable to see fifty feet in any direction."

To avoid becoming hopelessly lost, they decided to find a particular lake that could be identified in the aerial photos and serve as a reference point:

"As we moved ahead, in the direction of a glitter that must turn out to be water, we were startled to see an unmistakable flash of white just beyond. A second later it had assumed a strikingly familiar outline and we were staring straight at an adult whooping crane! Then, in another moment, we saw a second bird. . . . Both birds were very alert and they were moving in opposite directions, one to the left and one to the right. The bird to the right quickly disappeared behind the thickets, but the other whooper kept in view, although walking away from us with long strides. As we came out on the open shore of a little pond he rose from the brush on the other side, calling a series of alarm notes. Immediately he was attacked by a short-billed gull, which must have had downy young hidden along the edge of the pond. Wheeling in a short circle, and still calling, the whooper was soon out of sight. . . ."

Allen and Stewart spent ten more days at the nesting ground exploring the surrounding country, collecting plants and samples of the animal life of the ponds, and listing the birds and mammals that share the summer home of *Grus americana*. Allen's notes on the sights and sounds paint a vivid picture: "High ground, rises like islands above the surrounding confusion of ponds . . . Fires have swept over them . . . The only live trees that remain are clustered about wet depressions or along the course of the river. . . . The Sass is deep and swift and the water appears quite dark . . . Upstream, in a meager growth of poplars, there was a deserted beaver dam and the series of little water falls made a pleasant and somewhat drowsy music. Other songs were contributed by the birds in the river thickets—chiefly song sparrows, Lincoln's sparrows and redwings—while snipe winnowed in the twilight that passes for night in that latitude, and bitterns boomed from marshy ponds. . . . Now and then we heard the guttural notes of sandhill cranes and on a few occasions, the clear trumpet calls of whooping cranes. . . .

"Other birds were seen on the open burn—sparrow hawks, rusty blackbirds, juncos, chipping sparrows and flickers. A pair of lesser yellowlegs had built a nest on the moss-covered ground not far from our tent. . . .

Once a bald eagle flew over and twice we saw ravens soaring, gliding and stooping in the wind.

". . . The weather was hot and dry, the thermometer reading 92° Fahr. at 6 P.M. on the 23rd, and frequently starting the day in the low 80's. . . . Elsewhere there was heavy rain and violent electric storms. . . . We were thankful that the storms had passed us by, for our campsite and surroundings were as dry as tinder."

The bottoms of the ponds were too soft and spongy to risk crossing, but it was possible to walk along their rims: "We discovered small numbers of fish in some of the larger ponds . . . which we had not expected." Frogs were numerous. "No snakes were noted. Mollusks were very abundant and nine species were collected from the crane ponds. These creatures, and the frogs, must be important items in the whooping crane's diet."

Allen found that the mammals include the red fox, moose, black bear, and wood bison but that probably none is plentiful there.

Despite their constant watchfulness during these ten days, Allen and Stewart saw no more whooping cranes, though they heard their calls and found their seven-inch footprints, mingled with the smaller prints of the young, on the shores of the ponds. The birds seemed deliberately to stay out of sight. Allen wrote: "It was maddening to know that at least one pair of whooping cranes, with young in tow, was within a half mile of us most of the time, yet we were unable to watch them. Our visions were filled with them, a hundred yards away perhaps, calmly picking up snails, the young one quite possibly darting after a white admiral butterfly! Earthbound and weary, we could not tell. But we were on the spot. We had gazed at its features and felt of it with our bare hands. It is real and it is reasonably understandable. But most important of all, it is no longer unknown."

On July 2 a radio message told them that their helicopter would pick them up that afternoon. Allen and Stewart broke camp and lighted a smoky fire to guide their pilot. He arrived late that afternoon. This time the return to their old home base—the Hotel Mackenzie at Fort Smith—was triumphant. For Allen, the finest fruit of the expedition was the assurance that the whooping cranes could hardly have chosen a better place to rear their young in isolation and safety. He was satisfied that food and water were adequate and predators scarce. Fire, which had seemed a possible threat, would be stopped by the wet ground surrounding the nest sites. Allen wrote to Baker: "It is in truth a lost and unknown place, and the nesting whoopers should continue to prosper here . . . as they have evidently done for so many years. Only man can reach them here and do them harm, and, if not permitted to fly low over these ponds or land beside them by helicopter, even man need not be feared."

As the finale of his visit to crane country, Allen made a flight from Fort Smith over the territory he and Stewart had explored on the ground. To their delight they spotted two pairs of whooping cranes, each with twin young. The existence of two sets of twins made Allen wonder how often twin young reach flying age but die on the migration route. Only five times in the previous sixteen years had twins arrived at Aransas, and there had never been two sets in the same year.

After Allen had left for Florida, William Fuller continued to survey the crane nests. On one flight he saw eleven adults and six young. He last saw cranes in the area on October 12th, much later than Allen or anyone else had imagined they would remain.

Only twice in whooping-crane records had as many as six young birds reached Aransas from the nesting grounds. Thus Fuller's discovery of such a crop was fine news. In fact this, plus Allen's findings on the safety of the nesting grounds, would have made the outlook for *Grus americana* seem unusually bright were it not that all through the summer the United States Air Force had been relentlessly grinding ahead with a plan that, if carried out, promised a sudden end to the whooping cranes' sanctuary at Aransas and thus, inevitably, to the cranes as well.

14

The first news of the air force's threat to Aransas came in the early summer of 1955. At approximately the same moment that Robert Allen and his companions were struggling through the Canadian wilderness, the air force announced its intention to use the bombing range on Matagorda Island for practice in photoflash bombing. Photoflash bombs are spectacular devices used at night to illuminate large target areas. Their effect on wildlife has been demonstrated. Every creature that can walk, fly, or crawl leaves the vicinity with all possible speed. The use of the bombs at the edge of the Aransas Refuge would have emptied it of wildlife with dramatic suddenness.

In order to begin Project Photoflash, however, the air force found that it would be necessary to extend the danger area on both sides of the range. This was highly fortunate, for, instead of simply going ahead and dropping the bombs, the air force had to announce its plan and request that additional waters both on the Gulf and in San Antonio Bay be closed to traffic. As is required in such cases, a local public hearing was held by the United States Corps of Engineers.

Here again luck was on the side of wildlife, for this proved to be one of the rare occasions when the interests of commerce and cranes were united. Neither the local oil interests, real-estate interests, nor fishing interests were at all pleased with the air force proposal. Their opposition resulted in a second hearing. By this time virtually all national conservation organizations, including of course the National Audubon Society, had mobilized their opposition. The United States Fish and Wildlife Service called the attention of the air force to the presence of the whooping cranes, and also entered its protest. The outcome of this combined opposition was that the air force, in due time, decided to go ahead with its plan.

During the summer the controversy simmered on. Most of the activity was now behind the scenes: letters, telephone calls, pleading, exhortations, and various forms of wirepulling by conservationists, all of which apparently left the air force unmoved. The Fish and Wildlife Service had emptied its arsenal quite early in the game. Dr. Cottam, who had retired from the service the year before but was still deeply interested in the whooping cranes, recalls that he upbraided his former colleagues for not carrying the struggle further. If the project went through, he told them, they might just as well cut the whooping cranes' throats and get it over with.

When rescue for the cranes came it arrived, as usual, at the eleventh hour. Without doubt Robert Allen's hard work in Canada that summer had a great deal to do with saving the cranes. Had he given up and failed to find the nests there would have been very little whooping-crane news in the papers. As it was, his discovery brought the birds greater publicity than ever before. The New York *Herald Tribune* had sent John O'Reilly, an old friend both of Allen and of whooping cranes, to Canada to cover Allen's expedition. O'Reilly's vivid stories brought the whooping cranes worldwide attention. Canadians, particularly, became proudly aware that they were custodians of something rare and beautiful. Thus they were unpleasantly startled to learn, so soon after a dramatic triumph in conservation, that the precious birds were about to be blasted out of their southern sanctuary. Somehow, the Canadian newspapers felt, this didn't make sense; particularly when the blasting was a mere by-product of military convenience. Such headlines as THREAT TO WHOOPERS ALARMS OTTAWA—U.S. BOMB RANGE PROTESTED, appeared in Canadian papers. Canadian politicians, in turn, proved to be more sensitive to the protests of their citizens than had those in Washington. On October 20 the Canadian Embassy in Washington sent a formal note to the United States State Department: "The Canadian Ambassador presents his compliments to the Secretary of State of the United States of America and has the honor to draw his attention to a proposed photoflash bombing range. . . . It is hoped that the existence of the whooping crane will not be imperiled at a time when the prospects for the increase of the species have at last become bright."

John Foster Dulles, to whom this note was addressed, may have other distinctions in histories of the times, but it is nonetheless to his credit that ten days later, on November 1, this reply was delivered to the Canadian ambassador: "The Secretary of State presents his compliments to His Excellency the Ambassador of Canada and has the honor to acknowledge the receipt of his note No. 657 of October 20, 1955, drawing attention to reports of a proposed Air Force photoflash bombing range. The Department of State informed the Department of Defense of the Canadian concern, and has now received a reply stating that the Department of the Air Force is withdrawing its proposal for extension of the Matagorda Island Air Force Range, which is the matter referred to in the Ambassador's note."

At the moment that their survival was being decided at the highest diplomatic level, the whooping cranes were in flight between Canada and Aransas, running the gauntlet of gunfire that Allen was now convinced was the major cause of attrition. Once again the National Audubon Society made an effort to spread the word of the cranes' special status to hunters along the migration route. A leaflet describing the cranes and their plight was widely distributed. Local editors took up the cause, printing the leaflet's closing words: "We Appeal to the Sportsmanship and Humanity of Every Person, From Saskatchewan to Texas, to Withhold His Fire, and to Give Any Large White Bird God-speed, Instead of a Charge of Shot."

This autumn, of course, there was particular suspense as to whether the six young, seen in Canada, including the two sets of twins, would come through safely. On October 18, Julian Howard found that the first pair of cranes had arrived at Aransas. They had one youngster with them. In the next two weeks several singles and childless pairs drifted in. Then, on November 3, Howard saw the first set of twins, as well as three pairs of adults with one young each. The next day, to the delight of the whooping-crane circle, the second pair of twins was seen with its parents on Matagorda Island. By December, 1955, the grand total was eight young, the largest number of young to come through safely since crane records began, and twenty adults, representing a loss of only one adult bird. To the anxious bystanders it almost seemed as though the cranes themselves had, in some eerie way, responded at the right moment. Their unprecedented crop of young, and their good luck on the skyway, had once again staved off disaster.

Eventually the fate of the lost bird became known when the service got word that a whooping crane had been shot at a lake near Sioux Falls, South Dakota. One of a party of hunters shooting from a blind brought it down with a kill of snow geese. According to newspaper stories the hunter was arrested by game wardens.

As the cranes settled down at their winter quarters, Howard noted that the summer's events inspired more letters, telephone calls, and visits to Aransas than ever before. Hardly a day went by without someone phoning the refuge to report a stray flock of whooping cranes, which most often proved to be sunbathing pelicans. Most of the public feeling about the cranes was friendly to them, but there was a sprinkling of humorists and, what was more sinister, there were a few people who were furiously hostile. In the first category, one would suppose, was the lady who mailed an envelope of white chicken feathers to Aransas with a note advising the service that it could cease its search for the missing whooping crane. A Louisiana man sent a carton of pelican bones labeled "fossil whooping crane." On the hostile side was a letter, printed in a Corpus Christi newspaper, from a man who signed himself "Disgruntled," complaining about the attention lavished on a handful of birds. From here and there samples of hate mail reached Allen, and some of them made his blood run cold. A farmer in Saskatchewan proposed to put a stop to the fuss by killing the few remaining birds and thus saving both farmers and taxpayers further trouble.

Although Howard had counted twenty-eight whooping cranes on December 22, 1955, he was thereafter never able to locate more than twenty-seven. In his report on refuge events in the first quarter of 1956, he noted that two barren pairs had shown signs of being loosely united, and he guessed that one of these had lost a member. Because no corpse was found, the cause of the bird's disappearance was never known.

In April, as the cranes were leaving the refuge, Howard saw an oil slick drifting to shore from an offshore rig. He found that the contractor had washed down his equipment with diesel oil. Howard called in Texas game wardens, and the violator was ordered to install proper drip pans under his machinery.

On May 3, Howard found that all but three whooping cranes had left the refuge. A lone immature crane lingered on Matagorda Island where a family had wintered, and there was still a pair on the refuge. Shortly thereafter the tardy pair took wing, but got no farther than Lampasas County, Texas, where one of the birds collided with a high wire and crippled one wing. Its mate voluntarily came to earth with it, and the two cranes took refuge by a farm pond on a ranch owned by a Mr. Ed Kirby. For some weeks Kirby noticed the two huge white birds feeding at the edge of the pond, which was shrinking in the summer heat. At length the pond dried up entirely. After a day or two without water, the uninjured whooping crane deserted its mate and flew away. The cripple, driven by thirst, approached a water tank near the ranch house. Mr. Kirby chanced to see it, took his lariat, neatly slung the rope around the crane's neck, and dragged it into the house. Mrs. Kirby gave the captive food and water while Mr. Kirby telephoned the San Antonio Zoo and told Fred Stark that he had a big white bird tied up in his kitchen. Stark quickly dispatched a truck that brought back to the zoo the captive whooping crane now known as Rosie. Stark guessed by the size and conduct of the bird that it was a female and, because of the character of the markings on its head, thought it to be a yearling.

Although the circumstances that brought Rosie to Stark's zoo were similar to those that had brought Josephine to New Orleans, Stark made no effort to claim her as his property. After a conference with Fish and Wildlife officials in Washington, it was arranged that Rosie would remain at the zoo on loan from the service. She was assigned a large cage with running water and began what proved to be a nine-year wait for her nuptial day.

In the summer of 1956, Julian Howard was transferred, and in the autumn a new manager, Claude F. Lard, took his place at Aransas. It had been another hot, dry summer, and by autumn the water situation was very bad along the whole Texas coast. During November, conditions of food and water were growing ever worse and, as usual in this situation, the newly arrived cranes moved about so much that it was difficult to count them. It was at last clear that only two young had come through from Canada. Just as sad, there were only twenty-two adults. Of the twenty-eight of the year before, one was in the San Antonio Zoo; one was the bird that had disappeared from the refuge without trace; and four had been lost in the migration of 1956. Thus, in only one year, the seesaw of the cranes' luck had again tilted from high to low.

Nor was Aransas exactly an ideal refuge that winter. Lard reported to Washington in December, 1956: "All ponds and small lakes on the Refuge were dry until latter part of December . . . the only fresh water was the overflow of windmills. Every place we had a little fresh water we had an enormous concentration of ducks and geese, and the fresh water soon became a dirty looking green from overuse and we were afraid we would get an outbreak of disease at any time."

Lard also reported that the lure of the cranes brought an all-time high of 9,309 visitors to the refuge. Those registered were only a fraction of the so-called "visitor load," the tally of visits rather than individuals, which was estimated to be about 15,000. There were also unregistered visitors who were potentially a menace to the cranes, but the service had to rely on state officers, who seldom took court action against them. Lard recorded three cases of trespass on crane territory, and added, "The entrance of visitors and fishermen into unauthorized areas is very common despite the fact that all roads are marked off limit."

Lard's notes echo the warnings that Allen had expressed in his memoranda to Washington eight years earlier, warnings that had been almost entirely ignored. By this time, of course, Allen's official work on the cranes had ended. Little by little he had been made aware that his continued comments on what he considered the service's neglect of the cranes at Aransas were less than welcome; nevertheless he continued to visit the refuge and express his views. In the summer of 1956 he wrote to John Baker: "I was shocked at what I saw there last March. Much can be done . . . and would greatly benefit the whooping cranes. They need all the breaks we can arrange for them."

15

Meanwhile, at New Orleans Josephine and Crip had come through the year in a chicken-wire enclosure, a hundred feet square, behind the elephant house. Josephine was now more than sixteen years old; how much more no one knew. Some observers thought she must surely have come to the end of her reproductive span. Dr. Cottam, for one, was doubtful of her ability to carry on. However, on April 28, 1956, Josephine laid an egg on the bare earth in the same spot that she had made her ill-fated effort the year before. On May 2 she laid another egg, and then she and Crip began the month-long ritual of incubation. As the magic day drew near, the newspapers became increasingly interested. Again George Douglass found himself host to reporters and photographers. The slate roof of the elephant house overlooking the crane yard became a lookout post and press room from which the visitors watched the nest, forty feet below, and waited for the drama of hatching to take place.

At about the same time Robert Allen had come down with a second illness, as yet undiagnosed, and was in bed in Florida. John O'Reilly, who spent a week perched on the roof reporting on the cranes, sent him an account of events. In the first place, he wrote Allen, it is obvious that whooping cranes will eventually get used even to the strangest surroundings. All the odd sights and sounds of the zoo had become routine to the birds, and did not alarm them, but anything that did not fall into the raucous pattern was a disturbance. When O'Reilly's hat blew off and sailed to the ground, Crip rushed to the fence, ready to attack, and Josephine rose nervously on the nest.

The two parents shared the incubation as they had at Aransas. Crip was a cooperative partner, and came over promptly when Josephine gave her low call. At each relief the bird taking over rolled the eggs carefully with its beak. From time to time they pulled dried grass up around the eggs, and although there had been no nest when the eggs were laid, by the time hatching was near there was a mat of dried grass beneath them.

On what turned out to be the final day of incubation both birds were very tense. Josephine would not allow Crip to sit on the nest, but he

Sometimes when Josephine brooded her chick its fluffy head would pop out from the shelter of her wing.

stood over her as though on guard. At about 10:15 on the morning of May 29, the rooftop spectators saw Josephine get up and turn the eggs. A hole was visible in one of them. Four hours later, when she rose again, they saw a wing sticking out of the egg and, half an hour later, at 2:36, she got up, and a chick emerged from the broken shell. It was tiny, brown, and wet. Josephine called Crip, who had moved off to feed. He came to the nest. Both birds put their beaks together, pointing downward, then slowly stretched their necks skyward and gave a long, bugling call. The chick quickly dried out and became fluffy. It spent most of its first two days buried in Josephine's feathers while she incubated the second egg.

The chick's progress was astonishing. In two days it seemed to double in size and then was strong enough to leave the nest and flounder around in the grass. During this period Josephine's allegiance seemed to be divided between feeding the chick and incubating the remaining egg. Crip was greatly concerned over the chick. He kept close to it as it ran about, and he was constantly treading the grass, with toes extended, to flush out grasshoppers and other insects. When he caught a morsel he would mash it with his beak and then hold it at the tip of his beak in front of the chick's beak. The chick grabbed at the food readily, and, if it were a large piece, gobbled and gulped like a robin swallowing a worm.

The second egg hatched four days after the first, and another tiny crane emerged. From time to time both parents left the second chick in the nest while they wandered about the pen, feeding the first. Occasionally Josephine would return to the nest as though to check up on the younger chick. At night both little birds crawled into Josephine's feathers.

The second chick lived only two days. It vanished overnight, presumably the prey of an owl that could have swooped into the roofless cage, or perhaps carried off by one of the big rats that reporters had seen scuttling about the zoo. After the loss of the chick, Douglass had a wire top installed on the pen.

Poor Douglass, now in the embarrassing position of having failed in the care of the precious birds for a second time, while all the world watched, as it were, through the eyes of the reporters and cameramen assembled on the slate rooftop, was considerably upset. One of the reporters later wrote Allen his observations of the scene: "The more I think about it the more astonishing the whole thing becomes. In the first place it was ironic that a New Orleans politician should be the one under whose supervision the hatching took place. Douglass is a well-meaning guy, but his thirty-one years as a city employee have not prepared him for anything so vital as having nesting whooping cranes under his care. However, he is aware of his shortcomings in animal husbandry. He has no veterinarian at the zoo. If an animal gets sick he gets in touch with Stark or George Vierheller, or somebody who specializes in the branch to which the sick animal belongs, and asks them what to do about it. In an emergency he calls in a professional vet. I don't think he fully realized the significance of a successful crane nesting until the eggs were in the nest and national interest began to manifest itself. Then it was too late to improve the chicken wire pen in which Crip and Josephine were housed. As events progressed Douglass became more and more concerned. He would squat on the roof during the daytime and return to the zoo at night, sleeping but little and at the same time trying to keep up with his other duties as director of the park and swimming pool."

The result of all this strain was that the unfortunate zoo keeper came down with a stomach-ulcer attack, and was hospitalized.

The surviving whooping-crane chick grew rapidly. Within a few weeks it was a long-legged, ungainly youngster with tremendous feet and fluffy plumage colored cinnamon and buff. Its eyes were brown, rather than the acid yellow of its parents' eyes. It seemed to be always hungry, and the adults foraged for it, digging up the dirt of the pen in a search for earthworms. When the keeper filled their food pan the parent birds picked out shrimp and crab, which they broke up and presented to the chick with the tips of their beaks. Sometimes Crip or Josephine would throw a morsel on the ground and prod it until the chick noticed it and picked it up. Both birds were constantly vigilant, and fierce to intruders. When an unfortunate gray squirrel got into the pen, Josephine attacked it. The little beast barely escaped alive.

As the month of June wore on, there was increasing sultry heat. The chick seemed to tire easily and often dropped to its haunches to rest in the shade of a camphor tree, which was the only shelter from the blazing sun. In the first week in July one of the keepers noticed the chick sitting and gasping for air. By the second week it was doing this frequently. On the morning of July 13 the keeper saw the chick lying prostrate in the yard. He entered the cage, fending off the attacks of the parents with a chair, and picked up the little bird. It was quite dead. Autopsy showed it had died of aspergillosis, a fungus of the lung that afflicts domestic poultry. It had lived forty-five days, was thirty-three inches tall, and weighed four and three-quarter pounds.

Dismay over the little chick's demise was not limited to the immediate family, as it were. The circle of those interested in whooping cranes had been widening rapidly. Other zoo keepers, aviculturists, and an assortment of scientists and conservationists, both American and Canadian, had become intrigued with the problem of *Grus americana*. To some of these people the failures at New Orleans seemed to indicate that success in breeding whooping cranes in captivity was tantalizingly close, but could, in fact, be achieved only with more skillful handling than seemed possible under George Douglass's direction. A variety of proposals were made: that the service take Crip and Josephine by court proceedings, and, since the service possessed no avicultural facilities of its own, put them in the custody of someone qualified to try to raise captive whooping cranes; that adults be captured from the wild flock at Aransas to start a breeding experiment in another zoo and perhaps provide a mate for Rosie, whose sex was still undetermined; that young whooping cranes be captured at Aransas and distributed to zoos, or to private aviculturists, who might have the technical skill to raise them and breed a new generation; that eggs be taken from the whooping-crane nests in Canada and artificially incubated.

Since the Fish and Wildlife Service showed no disposition to make a legal issue of Josephine's custody, those interested in captive breeding of whooping cranes were led more and more to think of taking birds from the wild. In this way the fate of the wild birds was becoming entwined with the fortunes of the captives at New Orleans.

The question had of course been simmering for some years. By 1953, the idea of capturing whooping cranes had been urged often enough so that Allen had felt it worthwhile to express his strong feelings against it. In *Audubon Magazine* he wrote: "A few well-intentioned people have suggested that the wild cranes ought to be trapped, their great wings pinioned and the entire flock grounded on the Aransas Refuge in Texas. . . . We can fully understand the feelings that have inspired this plan but we would deplore its execution . . . it would be a fool-hardy and dangerous experiment, even if two or three birds were successfully caught, the loss and injury and the scattering of others would be a most deplorable price to pay for highly dubious results."

Allen's opposition had not, however, altered Dr. Ripley's conviction that only aviculture could save the whooping crane, and Ripley had in turn convinced a number of people whose opinion carried weight in conservation circles. Nor had Allen been able to persuade his old friend John Lynch (who in addition to his work as a Fish and Wildlife Service biologist was an aviculturist and privately raised waterfowl) that talk of capturing whooping cranes was doing more harm than good. Lynch had been studying the population figures of the Aransas flock, and concluded that without artificial aid the wild whooping cranes were unquestionably doomed. Meanwhile, in Canada, Fred Bard, of the Provincial Museum in Regina, who had maintained his interest in the whooping cranes ever since his efforts ten years before to find their nests, was likewise positive that the cranes were fluttering their last and that the remnants of the flock must be captured before it was too late to preserve them even in zoos. Like Ripley in the United States, Bard worked in Canada to line up support for this point of view.

In June, 1956, those in favor of captive breeding of cranes brought the issue to the fore at a Canadian meeting of wildlife managers—the Twentieth Federal-Provincial Wildlife Conference. United States representatives had been invited, but neither Allen nor Baker was able to go. Allen, still ill at his home in Florida, prepared a rebuttal to the arguments that he knew Lynch would present.

Allen's paper, read aloud in his absence, opened up the touchy question of whether an avicultural program could honestly hold out any hope of ever returning zoo-reared birds to the wild, or would in fact be merely a means to preserve specimens of the whooping crane in perpetual captivity. This, Allen was convinced, would be the inevitable outcome.

"The time has not yet come," Allen wrote, "for taking such drastic and perhaps dangerous action as suggested in these plans. . . . It is not our wish to see this noble species preserved behind wire, a faded, flightless, unhappy imitation of his wild, free-flying brethren. We are dedicated to the job of preserving the whooping crane in a wild state. We do not feel . . . that we have failed in this. If the day comes when we have reason to feel otherwise, then that will be time enough perhaps, for someone to consider such improbable techniques as capturing all young-of-the-year by running them to earth with helicopters (as has been seriously proposed!), sorting them out in rearing pens, pushing them to lay several sets of eggs, which would then be incubated artificially, and produce whooping cranes—or what would presumably pass for whooping cranes—like so many mallard ducks or barnyard chickens! No! The whooping crane faces enough dangers without turning it over to such an uncertain program as that."

However, of the two points of view Lynch's turned out to be the more persuasive. The conferees, most of them Canadian Fish and Game officers, voted to endorse Lynch's resolution that "a program of capture, artificial breeding and subsequent release to the wild" be undertaken for the whooping crane. Allen's proxy vote, cast by the representative who had read his paper aloud, was the only dissent.

An odd footnote was appended to the proceedings when someone mentioned that among those in the audience was Mr. Fred Bradshaw, the man who had found the last whooping-crane nest in Saskatchewan in 1922 and, as Allen had written, immortalized its tiny occupant with a numbered tag.

Following this meeting the National Audubon Society girded itself for what it saw as a battle to defend the whooping cranes from their friends. Since wild whooping cranes could be captured only by the Wildlife services of the United States and Canada, or through their authorization, the opposed camps, pro- and anti-capture, went to work to try to convert officials of these services to their point of view. John Baker immediately wrote to the Chief of the Canadian Wildlife Service, who replied that though he agreed in theory with Lynch, he had strong reservations on the practical application of the plan, particularly when it came to "any molestation of the birds on their summer range." Perhaps the Canadians felt that if a debacle were to result, it would be preferable to have it take place elsewhere.

To John L. Farley, Director of the Fish and Wildlife Service, Baker wrote that "our Society is absolutely opposed to [Lynch's proposal], which we believe is based on an erroneous assumption [that the cranes are doomed in the wild]. We believe that if cranes are wanted by zoos and aviaries, the source should be the production of young by the present captives."

On this point, if no other, the National Society and Dr. Ripley were in agreement. Dr. Ripley had been convinced all along that if the service were sufficiently determined, a legal way could be found to transfer the two captives from New Orleans to more skillful hands and that healthy young whoopers would undoubtedly result from better care. Furthermore, he felt that the two precious birds, Josephine and Crip, were in truth natural resources belonging to the people of the United States and Canada, and should be so declared, even if it took an Act of Congress to do it. Privately, Dr. Ripley expressed the view that the Fish and Wildlife Service was paralyzed by bureaucratic terror of stirring up a ruckus over ownership of the cranes; that it was principally the fear that Douglass, if attacked, would appeal to his congressmen for help that prevented more vigorous action.

Following the Canadian meeting, Ripley continued his efforts to line up supporters who would in turn urge the Fish and Wildlife Service to capture whooping cranes.

In July, Ripley wrote to Fish and Wildlife Director Farley, expressing pleasure that Rosie had been put in the custody of Fred Stark at San Antonio, but added that "failing a parthenogenetic birth," the service should consider trapping a mate for this new addition to the captive ranks. He also tackled the issue of whether it might ever be possible to return captive-bred whooping cranes to the wild: "There is no pertinence to the discussion as far as I can see, as to whether in future captive-reared birds will or will not survive in the wild state. The situation has gone beyond that, and in discussing such peripheral and conjectural matters we lose sight of the basic question of whether we want future generations to see the species alive at all or merely stuffed in museums. In the future, *all* live whooping cranes may have to be in parks or preserves of one sort or another just as the Buffalo occur today."

It was, of course, exactly this facet of Ripley's view of the cranes' future that sent cold chills up Robert Allen's spine and prevented any rapprochement between the National Audubon Society and Dr. Ripley on behalf of the species.

In September the American Ornithologists' Union came partway into Ripley's corner with a resolution, at its seventy-fourth meeting, stating that "whereas the whooping crane, one of the most remarkable and spectacular birds of North America, is in imminent danger of extinction," the Department of the Interior and the Congress of the United States should provide funds for a full investigation "of all methods whereby this bird may be saved."

With pressure mounting "to do something" about the cranes, the Fish and Wildlife Service found itself uncomfortably wedged between the opposing forces. It met the dilemma by calling a meeting. Invitations were sent to all national ornithological and conservation organizations, and to the directors of several zoos and museums. At 9:30 A.M. on October 29, 1956, what Allen described as "some forty highly interested gentlemen" filed into a conference room in Washington to confer on the plight of the whooping crane. The forty included all shades of opinion in the whooping-crane capture controversy, ranging from Allen and Baker on the one hand to Ripley, Lynch, and Bard on the other. Like medical specialists at the bedside of an ailing patient, the conferees found themselves not only offering totally different remedies, but unable to agree on the condition of the patient. It was one of the ironies of the situation that both sides—pro- and anti-captivity—had backed themselves into corners on the outlook for *Grus americana.* The National Audubon Society, which had for so long been calling for help for the wild whoopers, now found itself declaring that their condition in the wild was sufficiently robust as to make the drastic step of capture unwarranted; while the captivity bloc was equally vehement in its contention that the species had more than one foot already in the grave.

When, seven hours later, the forty interested gentlemen filed out again, the only thing that had been decided was that the Director of the Fish and Wildlife Service would choose a committee to study the problems of the whooping crane and to offer advice to the service. Its members, chosen from among those present at the meeting, represented both sides of the captivity fence.

From the point of view of the National Audubon Society the creation of the committee, known as the Whooping Crane Advisory Group, was indeed a blow, since it elevated to the status of "advisors" people who had heretofore been merely spectators. There were no interment ceremonies, but, as it turned out, the birth of the Advisory Group marked the death of the Cooperative Whooping Crane Project, so idealistically conceived eleven years earlier.

Deepening Robert Allen's gloom as he left Washington was his conviction that the real purpose of some of the captivity proponents was to capture *all* young whooping cranes as they reached Texas in order to build up a large captive supply. Even such a firm believer in aviculture for cranes as John Lynch had been rather taken aback by the drastic elaboration of his original ideas. If, by any chance, the Fish and Wildlife Service yielded to the proposals of the aviculturists, the struggle of the wild cranes would indeed be at an end.

16

Early in 1957 the Fish and Wildlife Service was subdivided. A number of its departments were grouped within a new pigeonhole and given the unhandy title of "Bureau of Sport Fisheries and Wildlife." The director of the new bureau was Daniel H. Janzen, a veteran service administrator who had been a regional director in the Midwest. Janzen deputized his assistant, Dr. Frederick C. Lincoln, to take responsibility for whooping-crane affairs and to represent the bureau on the Whooping Crane Advisory Group.

Meanwhile Dr. Ripley had continued to ponder the stalemate at New Orleans, and concluded that as an interim solution it might be possible to move the mountain to Mohammed: if the birds couldn't be sent to a qualified aviculturist, then the next best thing would be to send an aviculturist to them. He and Fairfield Osborn, president of the New York Zoological Society, enlisted a retired bird keeper, George Scott, to supervise a nesting season at New Orleans. The bureau agreed to pay Scott's salary. All that remained then was to persuade George Douglass to accept outside guidance. Thus the subsequent chapter in the whooping-crane saga might have been entitled "The Wooing of George."

In February, 1957, Ripley and Lincoln flew to New Orleans to pay Douglass a visit, and found him a cordial and receptive host. The three men sat down for a chat in the crane pen, while Josephine and Crip circled them suspiciously. Douglass accepted the offer of Scott's help. He listened attentively as Ripley made tactful suggestions on ways to improve the food, housing, and sanitary care of the whooping cranes. Ripley and Lincoln left New Orleans well satisfied. Lincoln issued a cheering report to the Whooping Crane Advisory Group: "Mr. Douglass was most cooperative and eagerly accepted every suggestion. . . . Mr. Douglass makes no pretense of being an aviculturist. . . . The two birds are in excellent condition and Crip is already putting on occasional dances to which Josephine remains rather coy. Both Dr. Ripley and I were very much pleased with the conditions we found and with the attitude and interest of Mr. Douglass."

Dr. Lincoln's memorandum then moved on to the tricky matter of who really owned Josephine and Crip—a question that was being raised with uncomfortable persistence by some members of the Advisory Group. To answer it, Dr. Lincoln now resorted to a bit of word mincing perhaps designed to mean all things to all people and avoid the unpleasantness of a showdown with Douglass. The whooping crane, he said, is a migratory bird and cannot be possessed either in Canada or in the United States except upon definite authority in the form of a permit from either of the two services concerned. "Such being the case," he went on, "a statement of ownership either of the adult birds or of any progeny is more or less academic and can be determined when the occasion arises."

Josephine laid two eggs at the end of April, and on May 11 George Scott arrived to supervise the hatching. The nest in which the eggs lay was merely a small flattened pad of hay that Josephine had made by lying down and drawing the hay to her with her beak. It was placed precisely where it had been the year before, in an open, unprotected area of the enclosure. The fierce heat of the semitropical sun made the task of incubation a difficult ordeal. During the noonday hours the incubating bird sat with half-closed eyes, panting visibly. The eggs were rarely left uncovered for any length of time. The birds exchanged shifts without any particular ceremony. Ordinarily when one bird seemed to feel its turn was over it rose and the other willingly took its place. Scott noticed, and was amused by, an incident that was exceptional. On an especially hot, steamy day Josephine incubated, gasping in the direct noonday sun, while Crip stood nearby, preening comfortably in the shade of a tall bush. Finally Josephine arose and looked about. Somehow Crip managed to avoid noticing the cue to take over. He turned his back and stalked away. Josephine finally hurried over to the water pail, took a long drink, and walked resignedly back to the eggs.

At 9:25 A.M. on May 18, Scott saw that one egg had been pipped as the chick within cut a narrow chink in its shell. The day was extremely hot, but Josephine sat all morning. At noon she allowed Crip to relieve her for two minutes. At 2:30 P.M. Josephine rose and turned the eggs. Crip made awkward attempts to settle on the nest, but Josephine drove him off and resumed her place.

The hole was now much larger, and Scott had seen the chick moving inside the egg, but it wasn't until nearly midnight that the chick finally freed itself. The hatching had taken almost fourteen hours to complete. The next morning at dawn Crip came over and coaxed the chick from the nest while Josephine continued to incubate the remaining egg. The chick ventured only a few feet from the nest, and after twenty minutes found its way under Josephine's wing. On May 21, twenty-four hours after it had first pipped its shell, the second chick made its way out. It was dry and fluffy within an hour, and shortly made a daring excursion of six feet from the nest. It seemed more vigorous than the first chick even though its hatching had involved a longer struggle.

The chicks took their first food when they were approximately a day old. At this stage the behavior of the birds was recorded by William Conway, Curator of Birds at the Bronx Zoo, who had come to New Orleans especially to see the infant cranes. "The entire feeding process," he wrote, "is one that shows a delicacy of relationship and a degree of parental attentiveness that some ornithologists might be loath to credit to a bird." He noted how carefully the parent worked the food in its bill and then, gently and precisely, offered the small particle, perhaps a piece of shrimp or a dragonfly, putting it directly in front of the chick's bill without quite touching it.

If the chick failed to take it, the adult might cock its head and softly drop the food in front of the chick. The chicks at first pecked clumsily at the offerings, and then, with increasing strength, became more accurate. Unlike young songbirds, the whooping-crane chick doesn't beg

Josephine fed her tiny chick even while it nestled in her feathers. The solicitous parents constantly offer food to their young.

with fluttering wings and open beak, but the parents are so attentive that it is offered food almost constantly.

Conway was fascinated by the interplay that accompanied Josephine's brooding of the chicks. The process of bedding down for the night involved many preparations and false starts: "At 5:50 P.M. the male began a strange ritualized tramping procedure in an area of high grass [perhaps to flatten the grass as a precaution against predators, Conway guessed], Josephine joined in as the chicks wandered nearby. She drew grass and bedding toward the center of the area. At 5:58 she lay down and drew more bedding grass about herself. The youngest chick pushed at the long tertials extending back near her 'elbow' and gained entrance under her wing. Shortly a minor uproar took place high up in the feathers of the mother's back. A small, fuzzy head appeared and looked about. At 6:10 the chick tumbled out of its feather bed and Josephine arose." A half hour later Josephine again lay down, and both chicks crept beneath her. Suddenly the second chick popped out from the feathers of her neck and walked off to get a drink of water. When it had drunk, Crip offered it a bite to eat, and the chick, thus distracted, began to follow Crip, looking up as though it hoped to be brooded, and eventually uttering a soft, cricket-like, twittering distress call.

Josephine, who had in the meantime been trying to call the chick to her side with a low, murmuring sound, now arose and went to fetch the errant one. Then, finally, the family settled down for the night. Throughout the hours of darkness Crip stood silently some three or four feet away, awake and alert for possible danger. In fact, for the first five days of the chicks' lives he was never seen to lie down.

Despite their parents' assiduous care, the young whooping cranes were still at the mercy of chance. One day, for instance, there was a sudden, drenching rain. Josephine immediately lay down to shelter the chicks. The smaller found its way under her wing, "pushing toward a warmth that might mean life or death at this delicate point in its existence," Conway wrote, but the larger chick seemed unable to find an entrance, perhaps because of Josephine's injured wing. While it struggled Josephine showed great anxiety, jerking her head and calling, but seemed unable to assist the youngster. The chick was thoroughly soaked by the rain and finally took shelter under a large leaf on a nearby bush. Fortunately, it was not fatally chilled.

The chicks grew rapidly. At the end of a week they were seven inches tall, and with increasing strength showed increasing rivalry. Rising to their full fluffy stature, they would spar, each trying to grasp the other's bill and twist it. Occasionally Crip and Josephine became quite excited by these small battles. They would put their heads down close to watch, and then, throwing their heads high, sound a loud, rattling call.

Scott stayed on until August to care for the young birds. By then they had become strong enough so that their survival seemed assured, and he felt it safe to leave them in the care of regular keepers. The young whooping cranes had been named George and Georgette in honor of Scott and Douglass. Their survival not only made avicultural history but also gave people on both sides of the captivity controversy a new factor to think about.

In September, 1957, Dr. Lincoln issued a new memorandum to the Whooping Crane Group reflecting further thought, and possibly behind-the-scenes maneuvering, on the ownership of the captive cranes. "Final disposition of the two birds raised this year is of course a decision that must be made by the Director of this Bureau," the memo stated bravely. "The young birds probably can remain with their parents until next spring." As for Josephine and Crip, Lincoln wrote, it was his opinion that they had best remain at New Orleans. Josephine, he pointed out, was an old lady, over seventeen or eighteen years of age, who might not be productive much longer. The transfer from Aransas to New Orleans had been followed by four barren years, and another transfer might result in an interruption of her egg-laying. There were grounds for this thought: Aviculturists have noted that captive cranes of other species sometimes stop laying for a time after a change of scene. On the other hand, immediately after moving from New Orleans to the relative freedom of Aransas, Josephine had nested for the first time.

Meanwhile, Douglass appeared to be enjoying his new situation as the world's only whooping crane-breeder. At a meeting of the National Audubon Society at which he spoke on the "Reproduction and Rehabilitation of the Whooping Crane," he handed around feathers to the audience. "I have here something which I doubt anyone has seen and I'm going to ask our future Congressman down there if he'll step up and pass these around, because these are whooping crane feathers and these here are the feathers that are changing color from brown to white." Douglass also had photographs of George and Georgette. "This will show you a parent bird, and two young birds . . . and you will see them in the process of changing color. Oh, I would say in about another two months at the rate they're going they will be a total white!" Mr. Douglass may not have been a whooping-crane expert to begin with, but he was fast on the road to becoming one.

In the discussion period that followed, someone asked Douglass what would be done with George and Georgette when they matured.

"That's a serious question," Douglass replied. "There's been so much discussion about what we are going to do about them and the easiest way out is to say, well, we'll have to see what develops. . . . Now what would happen to the birds if we had a successful nesting year and we had, say, two more? That is in the future, but I want to say this; that the Audubon Park Commission and your speaker are not trying to have in Audubon Park an exclusive flock of whooping cranes."

Douglass also acknowledged: "It is quite possible that the birds could hatch elsewhere in this country and do as well. I don't think they could do better because of the condition of the birds, the plumage and their health, but I do believe we should not keep all our eggs in one basket. . . ."

Ten days after his platform appearance before the National Audubon Society members Douglass took part in another public ceremony in a way that made the whooping-crane circle shudder. On November 22, 1957, the United States Post Office issued a whooping-crane commemorative stamp. In New Orleans the day was marked by an elaborate program of ceremonies. Dr. Lincoln later ruefully informed the Advisory Group that the program had included the personal appearance of the whooping cranes from the Audubon Park Zoo. The cranes had shared the television cameras with two senators and several congressmen. "An incident that is to be regretted," Lincoln wrote, "as it brought much criticism not only on this Bureau but also on the Audubon Park officials. Fortunately the birds suffered no harm, but it is only in thinking of what might have happened that there was cause for alarm."

This episode later resulted in a formal recommendation by the Twenty-third North American Wildlife Conference that the captive whooping cranes make no more TV appearances, and be removed from their pens only with the approval of the Director of the Bureau of Sport Fisheries and Wildlife.

Meanwhile, the bureau's director, Daniel Janzen, had appeared on the same program at which Douglass handed around crane feathers, with a rueful story of his own to recount. This concerned an episode at Aransas wherein Janzen, new to the job of dealing with whooping cranes, had learned at first hand of the possibilities for disaster that somehow so often attend all efforts, no matter how well intended, to handle *Grus americana.*

The story began with a report from Aransas in the spring of 1957 that three whooping cranes had not joined the others in migrating, and seemed to intend to spend the summer together on the refuge. The three were a mated pair and a young single that had wintered alone on the King Ranch and had also failed to migrate the summer before. Hearing of this, Dr. Ripley urged Janzen to have the single captured during the summer while it was molting and flightless, with the hope that it might turn out to be a mate for Rosie, confined in sterile solitude at the San Antonio Zoo.

Dr. Cottam, who was now director of the Welder Wildlife Foundation at Sinton, Texas, a two-hour drive from Aransas, agreed with Ripley, and added the explicit recommendation that the tricky business of capture should not be left to the judgment of the refuge staff, but should be supervised by himself and Fred Stark. Under no circumstances, he warned, should the bird be captured in the heat of the day.

Janzen later told the Audubon Society members how, knowing himself to be green at the job, and knowing, too, the danger that the bird might be killed or injured in an attempt to capture it, he put off the decision as long as possible. Finally, in June, the refuge manager notified Janzen that because the three summering whoopers were in full molt, and unable to fly, it would be easy to drive them into a net. Janzen then gave his approval to the capture, but included the instruction that Cottam and Stark be on hand. Unfortunately, this last proviso was not fulfilled. On the morning of July 1 the refuge manager found the single bird separated from the pair, and decided to take the opportunity to capture it without bothering the other two birds, even though this decision allowed no time for Cottam or Stark to get to Aransas.

"Then," Janzen told the Audubon Society members, "I got a call from the refuge manager and he was in tears. And I don't blame him. What happened was this. . . . They put a net across one narrow spot, and they started to work these birds toward this narrow spot. . . . When they started to drive [them] . . . the bird cut off into some heavy brush, and [the men] moved up and captured the bird. The bird showed no sign of injury of any kind, and they took it to headquarters. The bird apparently was all right. Stark came out. He looked at the bird. He said, 'Well, it's breathing rather rapidly.' And about that time the bird collapsed. It apparently went back on its feet later on, and it was all right, and all of a sudden it collapsed again and it was dead within two hours."

The embarrassed Janzen went on to say that autopsy had shown that the bird had an enlarged spleen and was thin, but uninjured. Often, he said, in the capturing of wild animals a certain percentage keel over for no apparent reason. In this case the cause may have been shock, fright or exhaustion.

Dr. Cottam, who was indignant that the refuge manager had acted alone and sent for Stark only after the damage had been done, thought the unfortunate bird had died of heat exhaustion. John Baker did not let the episode pass unremarked. In view of this "complete fiasco," he wrote to Winston Mair, Chief of the Canadian Wildlife Service, he hoped there would be less talk about capturing wild whooping cranes.

Apparently the lesson was not lost on Janzen, for he told the National Audubon Society that he now felt the danger in capturing wild cranes was such that it would be better to wait and hope that an accidentally crippled bird would be saved to provide a mate for Rosie. "I am right now in the mood that we have two flocks of whooping cranes—those in captivity and those on the outside—and I am not disposed to capture any more wild birds. I say again 'disposed' because I feel that no decision ever made is ever final. You might find that later you may change your mind. . . ."

Meanwhile, the migrants who spent the summer of 1957 in Canada had a fairly successful season. The first pair returned on October 21. By November 14 the number of whooping cranes on the refuge had built up to twenty-six, of which four were young. One summer casualty was seen, crippled, on October 29 on Grand Lake, two miles north of Ketchum, Oklahoma. Unfortunately, the bureau didn't hear of it until months later, and by then it had disappeared. On November 17 another single was sighted in Manitoba, and the sighting verified by a staff member of Ducks Unlimited, but this bird never appeared at Aransas.

17

As the winter of 1957–1958 wore on, the problem of the captives at the New Orleans Zoo remained a vexing one for the bureau. Members of the Whooping Crane Advisory Group continued to press the bureau to find some way to take the birds away from Douglass. The bureau continued to temporize—as though it hoped to catch more whooping cranes with honey than with vinegar. In February, 1958, Dr. Lincoln visited New Orleans for another pleasant talk with Douglass. He presented him with a permit from the bureau authorizing him to keep Crip, Josephine, and their progeny. Bravely, but somewhat unrealistically appended to the permit was the condition that the bureau "reserved the right to take them into custody at any time."

Lincoln also discussed with Douglass the position of George and Georgette, whose sire, Crip, was indubitably government property. It was the consensus of opinion, Lincoln said, that the young whoopers should be moved to another zoo so that all the world's captive whooping cranes wouldn't be in one basket. The very excellent San Antonio Zoo was the first choice.

Politely, Douglass replied that his "curator of birds," was making a study of the plumage development of the young, so the transfer would not be convenient at that particular moment. Douglass's curator of birds had been recently hired and would not stay long, but he served his purpose, for there the matter rested.

In truth, it was far from safe to have the birds so concentrated, regardless of the care they received. A hurricane, an avian epizoötic, or even a bucket of spoiled shrimp mixed with their rations, could wipe them out at one blow despite the most careful guardianship.

A freak accident was always possible. An anecdote current in the whooping-crane circle described the visit of a northern zoo director to inspect the captives. Josephine was on the nest. There was knee-high grass in the pen, and the visitor remarked to Douglass that the grass might shelter rats or other predators. Douglass ordered a workman to cut the grass, and then led his colleague off to look at something else.

Shortly the two men heard a fierce bugling, and hurried back to the crane pen. Crip, in the full majesty of his protective fury, had hemmed the workman in a corner. Crip was lunging and thrusting at the man, who was swinging the blade of his scythe within inches of Crip's long, priceless neck, and crying, "Bird, you come closer and I'm gonna cut off your head!"

Lincoln had hoped that Scott would return to New Orleans to supervise the 1958 breeding season, but Scott was unable to come, and no other qualified man could be found. The regular care of Josephine and Crip was now in the hands of a new keeper, a kindly little man named Leo Buras, whose greatest avicultural qualification was his boyhood experience in raiding the nests of egrets and raising the nestlings. Leo and Josephine had something in common, in that many years before his arrival at the zoo a hurricane had blown Leo out of his birthplace, at the tip of the Delta, just as a storm had blown Josephine out of hers at White Lake. Leo wandered north to New Orleans, where he found work in a bakery making cookies. He baked cookies for thirty-seven years until the bakery closed in 1957. He then applied at the zoo and soon found himself cleaning birdcages. Then Leo, the small, gray-haired cooky baker, was gradually transmuted into a whooping-crane keeper, a job he has performed with great conscientiousness and the anxious manner of a man who lives in fear that the cookies may burn.

In the spring of 1958, Josephine laid four eggs. Three were infertile, but one was successfully hatched. Under the care of Leo Buras the third whooping crane to be born in captivity survived the perils of infancy. Leo christened the young bird Peewee. The world supply of captive whoopers now numbered five at New Orleans and, of course, solitary Rosie at San Antonio.

During the summer of 1958 the wild whooping cranes, as though to refute the charge that they couldn't possibly survive on their own, had nested with remarkable success. In the autumn the flock, which had numbered twenty-six in the spring, came back thirty-two strong. Four families with twin young and one single youngster made a total of nine young whoopers, the largest number in the twenty years that records had been kept. Actually, ten young had been produced. A young bird and an adult were sighted at the Mingo National Wildlife Refuge near Puxico, Missouri, after the others had reached Aransas, but they were never seen again. Two other adults also vanished. Thus the net gain to the flock was six. The increase seemed to Allen and Baker a splendid affirmation of what the whooping cranes could do on their own—given just a little luck, and protection from man.

It was indeed fortunate that the wild cranes had been able to help themselves, for no one else had been able to accomplish much in their behalf. One particularly sad failure was the defeat of a proposal to enlarge the refuge area at Aransas and rename it the Whooping Crane National Wildlife Sanctuary, thus giving the cranes top billing over ducks and geese.

Ever since Allen had discovered what he considered the immutable territorial requirements of the cranes, he had been troubled by the paradox at Aransas: If the cranes increased as everyone hoped they would, there would not be enough refuge land to accommodate them. The problem was, of course, compounded by the cranes' insistence on a certain type of habitat. Thus the possibilities for extra crane territory were narrowed to a very few: these were portions of Matagorda, St. Joseph, and Mustang islands and of the King Ranch. These lands were already being utilized by millionaire ranchers; men who were in the main sympathetic to whooping cranes, but whose sympathy was not sufficient to cause them to wish the refuge enlarged at their expense. In spite of this ready-made impasse, Congressman John Young of Corpus Christi and Senator Ralph Yarborough were persuaded to introduce the necessary bills in Congress. In December, 1957, H.R. 9353 was discussed at a public hearing in Corpus Christi. Opposition was expressed by a spokesman for the Sportsmen's Clubs of Texas, of which one of the millionaires in question, and owner of crane territory on Matagorda, happened to be president.

The spokesman, Cecil Reid, argued that while no one was more ardently in favor of aiding whooping cranes—or in fact all wildlife—than the sportsmen of Texas, they saw no need to enlarge the refuge, because the ranchers owning the lands adjacent to it were also keen conservationists who protected the cranes quite adequately. This argument changed Congressman Young's mind, and he has since then held the same view as the Sportsmen's Clubs of Texas. The bills died.

On a smaller scale, but on the same note, was John Baker's experience in trying to persuade the owner of St. Joseph Island to set aside a bit of whooping-crane territory there and post it against hunting. This project failed, thanks to the protests of a local man who rented out hunting boats and found the site a convenient one for duck blinds.

After being laid up for almost a year with his second bout of illness—which had finally been diagnosed as a rare metabolic disorder that could be controlled—Allen was able to go back to work late in 1957. In the autumn of 1958 and in early 1959 he returned to Aransas to check up on the cranes. It was distressingly apparent that despite his two years of work, and his carefully documented recommendations, the situation there was quite unchanged. Allen reported to John Baker: "I was impressed by the fact that the whooping cranes are pretty much left to shift for themselves. They receive no special attention. The only Refuge patrolman spends 90% of his time trapping wolves, coons, possums, and skunks!

Meanwhile, entire crews, with their families, housing provided, live on Aransas to look after the oil interests, the cattle interests, and the administrative affairs of the area, but not one solitary soul is there to tend to the welfare of the wintering whoopers. Actually this is nothing new, nothing we haven't faced before, but the point is there does not seem to be any official awareness of the problem and no effort to do anything about it."

Allen was also much concerned about a new menace to the cranes that had loomed up in the north. The Canadian National Railway had announced plans to build a branch line to reach zinc and lead deposits near Great Slave Lake. Two routes were possible. The shorter, and cheaper, would go through Wood Buffalo Park, and pass within eight or ten miles of the edge of the nesting grounds. If it were put through, Allen foresaw that the railroad would be likely to change the course and flow of rivers; start fires along the right of way that might sweep on to the nesting grounds; and bring in telegraph lines, which are always a hazard to large birds. Finally, and worst, it would provide ready access by people.

Once again the Canadian Audubon Society, and its friends, leaped to the defense of the cranes, and once again the issue of their safety was on the front pages of Canadian newspapers. This time, though, it would be more than two years before the final decision was made.

Meanwhile, the news from New Orleans had been especially tantalizing. On Valentine's Day, 1959, Josephine surprised everyone by laying an egg well ahead of schedule. Three days later she laid a second. She then proceeded to break one of the eggs and, picking up the broken pieces, carried them to the water trough and placed them in it. She broke her second egg and put it, too, in the water trough. Three days later, George Scott, who had agreed to supervise once more, arrived. Josephine laid a second clutch of eggs, which Scott took from her and put in an incubator. She then laid a fifth egg, which Scott left in the nest.

By April 15 the incubated eggs had passed the normal hatching period by almost a week. Scott opened one of them and found a partially formed chick dead inside it. By then the fifth egg, on which Josephine was setting, was within three or four days of maturity. Scott took it from the nest and put it with the egg that still remained in the incubator. Four days later, when it was obvious that nothing would emerge, Scott opened both eggs and found both rotten. Two weeks passed, and then Josephine laid a sixth and a seventh egg. Scott left them in the nest. Josephine and Crip incubated these for almost a month. Then, on June 3, Crip arose from the nest, revealing a broken egg. He picked up the shell in his beak and put it in the water trough. Scott was unable to tell if it had been fertile. On June 13, when the last egg was long overdue, Scott opened it and found a fully formed dead chick that for an unknown reason had been unable to escape from the shell.

This time there was no ready explanation for the disaster. For once Mr. Douglass could not be blamed, since Scott had been in attendance. It could only be hoped that Josephine's poor performance was simply an example of the uncertainty of raising whooping cranes, and not an omen for the future.

While the news from New Orleans was saddening to the entire whooping-crane circle, it made life particularly difficult for the Bureau of Sport Fisheries and Wildlife. Dr. Lincoln had hoped that if Josephine and Crip raised enough young to produce other mated pairs, Douglass would share some of the young with the other zoos and aviculturists who were pressing the bureau with increasing insistence. Not long before this, a number of aviculturists had joined together in an organization called the International Wild Waterfowl Association. Its president was Jean Delacour, the French-American scientist who had once given Douglass a testimonial. Dr. Ripley was vice-president. Soon after its creation the International Wild Waterfowl Association formed a standing committee to study the whooping-crane problem. This committee, which later decided to call itself the Whooping Crane Conservation Association, dedicated itself to making two basic points: (1) wild whoopers must be captured to create a breeding stock; (2) the bureau must somehow wrest some of the already-captive whoopers from Douglass's grip and, since the bureau possessed no facilities for raising cranes, spread them around among other zoos.

There was, of course, nothing the bureau would have liked better than to be able to settle the matter by removing the cranes from New Orleans—provided it could be done neatly and without fear of political reprisals. In April, 1959, Bureau Director Janzen asked the Solicitor of the Department of the Interior to look once again at the legal possibilities. In July the answer came back. The Solicitor stated that the United States had no title to the birds and—even sadder—no claim on the young cranes, George, Georgette, and Peewee.

During the winter months of 1958–1959 the wild whoopers, twenty-three adults and nine young, spent a quiet season without any loss, and began their departure on schedule in April. This year the bureau had assigned a biologist, E. L. Boeker, to appraise the cranes' situation. Boeker made a particular effort to discover just where the unmated yearlings wandered during the summer, for it seemed quite clear they did not come to the nesting grounds. There had been a growing suspicion that somewhere these young birds encountered unknown hazards and that an unduly small percentage of them survived to become breeders. In May and early June, Boeker searched likely portions of Saskatchewan by plane. Of the nine young whooping cranes that had left Aransas, he was able to sight only one bird. The summer whereabouts of the young remained as much of a mystery as the location of the nests had once been.

That spring the breakup of ice in the Sass River area was three weeks later than usual, and the weather that followed was unsettled. The Canadian Wildlife Service, which each summer made regular aerial inspections of the nest areas throughout the breeding season, was able to locate unusually few pairs and, what was worse, only one fledgling.

In October, as the cranes started their flight south, a series of early and severe storms struck the northern states and apparently forced the birds to change their route, for very few were sighted on the traditional path. True to the gloomy prediction from the Canadians, only two young reached Aransas. Fortunately, only one adult had been lost, so the flock was now thirty-three.

Meanwhile, Allen and Baker were still discussing, by mail, their dissatisfaction with what they considered the laissez-faire policy at Aransas —a policy the bureau would justify whenever it was criticized on this score by pointing out that whooping-crane mortality at Aransas was relatively small compared to summer losses.

In the autumn of 1959 Allen wrote Baker another memorandum: "All the old difficulties are still present and still unsolved. Trespass violations and buzzing by low-flying aircraft are completely out of hand. There seems to be no official consciousness of these problems and no long range plan for dealing with them. As the human population increases in that area they can only get worse."

In sixty days at Aransas, Allen had frequently seen trespassing fishermen drive the whooping cranes into the air. Twice he saw private planes buzz the birds as they fed. Air-force jets flew low over the refuge, but the cranes didn't seem to mind them. Regular practice bombing and target runs were taking place on Matagorda Island just east of Panther Point.

"The cranes occupied all available territories and are being pressed on every hand by the increasing human population," Allen wrote. He urged Baker to try once more to persuade the owners of Matagorda and St. Joseph, and the State of Texas, which controls Ayres and Roddy Island, Mullet Bay and Mustang Lake, to set these areas aside for the use of the cranes. The owner of St. Joseph was amenable, but his tenant was not. Allen's hope was partly realized, however, in 1960, when the National Audubon Society was able to lease 4,003 acres of Matagorda from Toddie Lee Wynne for the use of the cranes. The next year they subleased a further 1,717 acres from Mr. Wynne, thus giving the cranes the use of all the suitable marshes outside air-force territory. As a further safeguard the society placed the leased land in the care of a full-time warden equipped with a motorboat. Thus, for as long as the present owners control the land, and continue the lease, the cranes that use the island are protected, provided another war does not bring live bombing back to the bombing range.

Ironically, the human pressure at Aransas was being hastened by the whooping cranes themselves. Over the years publicity had made them an important tourist attraction. Dr. Cottam estimated that tourists visiting the cranes brought the State of Texas a million dollars a year. An excursion boat, the *Mary Lou,* out of the bayside town of Rockport, made a profitable business bringing sightseers to the cranes at five dollars a head. Traveling the Waterway through the refuge, the *Mary Lou* often brought the visitors within a stone's throw of the feeding whoopers. Later, as business increased, the *Mary Lou* was joined by an even larger craft, named the *Whooping Crane.*

Fortunately, a boat moving at a steady speed doesn't bother the cranes—nor is it likely that bird watchers would molest them—so this facet of the cranes' popularity was not a source of worry. Much more important was the increasing settlement of the whole area. Rockport was growing rapidly as a center for hunting, fishing, boating, and even bird-watching. The value of shorefront property was rising, and more and more the gay little flags of developers marked the places where bulldozers would roll into the brushland bordering the highway between Rockport and Aransas. Thus, when Allen visited Aransas in 1959 he found the picture vastly different from the wild, lonely emptiness of ten years earlier—and since then it has changed even more.

It was obvious to Allen that the chances of getting more space for the cranes would diminish with each passing year. In 1960, he wrote: "Each pair and family requires approximately four hundred acres. This fact I have checked and rechecked. If the flock increased to a hundred birds where are they to winter? I know that area and every acre surrounding it, and the only possible room for expansion is on Matagorda Island and possibly on St. Joseph, but the habitat there is limited. To tell the truth there is not much room to spare right now, and if we had as many as fifty birds to deal with they'd be hard put to it to find undisturbed, honest-to-God whooping crane habitat. It is a problem that has worried Baker and me for some time. It is something we've been trying to interest the Bureau of Fish and Wildlife in taking seriously."

A short time later Allen wrote in *Audubon Magazine*: "Do we really want to save the whooping crane? For the first time there is grave doubt by some people whether, for all our pious words to the contrary,

In 1951 Allen made a strenuous trip to Yucatán where this photograph was taken. With his death in 1963, the wild cranes lost their most ardent and learned champion.

we can continue to provide sanctuary for large, wilderness-seeking species like the whooping crane."

In this, for the first time, Allen seemed to be on the verge of admitting that defeat might be inevitable, no matter how he, or anyone else, labored to save *Grus americana.*

In June, 1960, Robert Allen retired from the National Audubon Society, for which he had worked for thirty years. His retirement at fifty-five was something he had long promised himself in order to work on his own writing and research projects unhampered by routine assignments. Once or twice more in the next three years Allen would make yet another effort on behalf of the cranes, but in truth his retirement marked the end of what he could do for them.

Allen continued to feel, passionately, that it was the wild flock of birds, not captive whooping cranes, on which attention should be centered; that it was the problem of helping the small flock increase its numbers beyond the danger point that presented the true challenge. In his monograph he had written: "As the human population curve goes up, the Whooping Crane curve goes down. This is a bird that cannot compromise or adjust its way of life to ours. Could not by its very nature; could not even if we had allowed it the opportunity, which we did not. For the Whooping Crane there is no freedom but that of unbounded wilderness, no life except its own. Without meekness, without a sign of humility, it has refused to accept our idea of what the World should be like. If we succeed in preserving the wild remnant that still survives it will be no credit to us; the glory will rest on this bird whose stubborn vigor has kept it alive in the face of increasing and seemingly hopeless odds."

After his retirement Allen lived in Tavernier, and in 1961 finished writing *Birds of the Caribbean.* He was making new studies of flamingos and spoonbills—his two greatest loves next to whooping cranes—when in May, 1962, he had a severe heart attack. He recovered from it and impatiently went back to work. He had a second heart attack, and died on June 28, 1963.

Robert Allen's work for the whooping crane had been the most profound involvement of his professional career. He had laid all he had, emotionally, physically, and intellectually, on the line in his effort to save the wild birds. They had come to symbolize some of his deepest moral beliefs regarding conservation. He was convinced that with the proper effort they *could* be saved—and yet—at the time he died—there was little in the fortunes of the whooping cranes to give him very great hope.

18

It would be difficult to choose any particular moment as a turning point in whooping-crane affairs, but it does seem that in 1960 a good many changes that had been in the making for some time took effect. Of these, by far the most important was the bureau's realization that it couldn't remain forever wedged between the upper and nether millstones of the aviculturists and the National Audubon Society, while the whoopers quietly faded away, but must indeed do something—if not necessarily what either suggested. Late in 1960 the bureau did what everyone now agrees was the right thing to do—it launched avicultural studies of its own. This program did not, of course, spring into being full-blown; it was a measure that had been persistently urged—in various forms—by almost everyone: the National Audubon Society, Dr. Ripley and his friends; and men within the bureau itself, for five years or more. In a sense the National Audubon Society and the aviculturists had worked together better than they knew; as opposing forces they had pushed the bureau in yet a third direction that combined elements of the course desired by each.

As far back as 1956, Dr. Ripley's gadfly tactics had forced the bureau to do some homework in preparation for its Whooping Crane Conference, and this included an effort to make an up-to-date biological assessment of the whooping cranes' situation. John Lynch had prepared an analysis of the cranes' vital statistics that was in turn given for review to another bureau biologist, a quiet, dark-haired young man named Ray C. Erickson. Dr. Erickson took his assignment with a seriousness and a thoroughness that hadn't been matched since Allen's studies. Erickson disagreed with Lynch's conclusions—since he thought it would be unwise to capture wild whooping cranes at that time, or allow any aviculturists to capture them—but suggested that the bureau should prepare itself for the eventuality by experiments with the whooping cranes' abundant cousins, the sandhills. Working with them it might be able to devise techniques of capture, rearing, and even reintroduction to the wild, that would show the way if the time ever came to capture whooping cranes. This suggestion for pilot studies with sandhills was put forward by Erickson in a memo to Janzen. Then, for almost five years, a short period as time is measured within government agencies, nothing tangible resulted.

As Erickson continued off and on to work at his whooping-crane assignment, studying whatever data came his way, he noticed a peculiar feature of whooping-crane statistics. On several occasions the population suffered a major loss of birds, yet the following year brought back as many young as ever. This led him to think that the losses had occurred not among mated pairs—the elders of the flock—but among the subadults, the wanderers of summer. It was this idea that prompted Boeker's efforts to trace them in the summer of 1959.

Erickson made still another interesting discovery. The major losses to the flock had occurred during years when the ground water level was high in the prairie provinces of Canada, filling the potholes that dot the land. Conversely, it seemed that during the dry years more adults—presumably yearlings—survived. Making a guess to account for this, Erickson put forward the idea that when the prairie potholes dried up, the yearling cranes flew elsewhere, possibly northward into the wet brush country, and for some reason prospered; while in wet years they stayed on the prairies and fell prey to farmers defending their wheat, to four-footed predators, or some unguessed danger. Supporting this surmise was the fact that cranes have been seen in the pothole country southeast of Regina only during wetter years. In Canada wet years usually run in cycles of two or three or more, during which ground water builds up. This, coupled with the amount of winter snowfall, makes it possible to predict, with reasonable success, whether prairie potholes will be full or empty in any coming summer.

Coupling the two ideas of high mortality of yearlings in wet summers—and the predictability of wet summers—Erickson came up with the proposal that four to six immature whooping cranes be captured at Aransas when a wet summer was in prospect. In this way it would be possible to acquire the breeding stock for which the aviculturists clamored and at the same time salvage birds that would otherwise quite likely be lost in their maiden season. He again urged that the groundwork be laid by experiments with sandhills.

In this work of Erickson's, the bureau saw hope of finding a way out of its dilemma. Biological studies accompanied by success in breeding sandhills might convince the Audubon Society of the rationality of capturing whooping cranes, and, at the same time, hold off the criticisms of the aviculturists. And last, but not least, it seemed possible that through experience with sandhills the whooping crane might indeed be saved.

In 1960 the bureau announced that it was going to begin its own propagation by the bureau of whooping cranes. Thus, for the first time in quite a long while the bureau was about to do something in relation to the whoopers with which few could find fault.

In the spring of 1960 Josephine and Crip had performed their nuptial dances within their cramped and arid quarters at the Audubon Park Zoo. Josephine began her annual effort to raise young. Her first three eggs were infertile. In mid-April she laid two more. On May 17 the first egg hatched a fine little chick. The second hatched on May 18. The next day the second chick was found dead in the grass. Douglass took the survivor from the parents and put it in a brooder, where it was fed by hand. It seemed to do well until, without warning, it collapsed and, as Douglass described it, "died without a struggle." Again aspergillosis was to blame.

At this time George and Georgette were approaching their third birthday. No one knows, exactly, when whooping cranes are old enough to mate, but since sandhills pair at three there was reason to think that the young birds were approaching maturity. Douglass began to view them hopefully for signs of difference in sex, but the young cranes, penned together since infancy, now showed quite the reverse of prenuptial behavior. From time to time one or the other would become excited and run back and forth against the side of the pen until its wings were raw. The birds calmed down as soon as they were separated. The two-year-old chick named Peewee, in a pen divided from the others by chicken wire, showed nothing but alarm in the company of its siblings.

Meanwhile, the wild whooping cranes had been continuing their uphill struggle with that strange, last-ditch tenacity that Robert Allen had termed a "vital intangible of the situation."

The drought at Aransas had broken in the summer of 1959 and been replaced by a protracted wet spell that was as bad for the cranes as the drought had been. Thanks to the dikes and channels that had been built on the refuge, floods of fresh water washed over the marshes, upsetting the precarious balance of salinity and destroying the marine life that usually provided the cranes with food. The thirty-three wintering cranes spent more time on the canal as the winter progressed, and then a number of them moved to Matagorda and St. Joseph. When the spring migration took place, a pair elected to stay behind and summer on Matagorda. In the summer of 1960, the nesting birds had above-average luck and that autumn brought back six young to the still-flooded refuge. The summer's loss was three and so there was a new record of thirty-six whooping cranes on the refuge.

Unfortunately, conditions on the refuge prevented any complacency. The cranes wandered far and wide in search of food, sometimes within the limits of the Matagorda bombing range. As in the previous year, heavy rains caused trouble in the marsh.

"The whooping cranes gave us nothing but fits," the manager wrote in his report on the 1960–1961 winter. "We attribute the cranes' strange actions to the fresh water intrusion. Fresh water was impounded behind the east shore road and released comparatively slowly through control structures and washouts to spread over the coastal marsh, polluting the tide pools and lakes which are normally whooper food lockers." In an effort to keep the cranes on the refuge, the manager dropped paper bags full of wheat on the marshes, thus at last putting into effect one of Allen's suggestions. "Whoopers took readily to this supplemental feeding," the manager reported, "and more than once were observed rushing to the air-dropped wheat."

Before the eventful year 1960 ended, there had also been important changes in the personnel of the whooping-crane circle. John Baker followed Robert Allen into retirement, and became president emeritus. His place was taken by Carl Buchheister, a graduate of Johns Hopkins, and former teacher, who had served the society in various ways for years.

The circle also lost Dr. Lincoln, who died in September. The crane portfolio was handed on to the bureau's Assistant Director Lansing Parker, a tall, genial administrator who had been in the service since 1945. Parker picked up where Lincoln had left off in the ticklish job of maintaining polite communication with Douglass, with the aviculturists, represented by the Whooping Crane Conservation Association, and with the bureau's old friend and critic, the National Audubon Society.

In the spring of 1961, Parker had pleasant news to report. Josephine laid four eggs, and though three were infertile the fourth hatched a healthy young whooping crane that gave every promise of surviving. The fourth whooper born in captivity was named Pepper.

In the spring of 1961, the wild cranes left their flooded home at Aransas early and departed for Canada where, though they could hardly have been aware of it, luck had turned to their side. Protests over the proposal to put a railroad line near the nesting ground had reached the highest political levels. Prime Minister John Diefenbaker, in a speech from the throne, had asked Parliament to appropriate funds to survey the western route that would detour Wood Buffalo Park. At considerable cost, this route was adopted. The summer was fortunate in other ways also. Only two birds were lost, and five young returned in the autumn of 1961. Again there was a new record: thirty-nine cranes. Meanwhile, in September, Hurricane Carla had swept the refuge, erasing many of the works of man and recharging the salt flats with seawater and crabs.

As winter wore on, the members of the flock wandered about, even though there was plentiful food on the refuge. Perhaps their high number caused their restlessness. In December the foreman of the ranch on Matagorda found a dead whooping crane on the island, a discovery he decided to keep to himself. When, months later, the news got out and the refuge manager learned of it, the foreman explained his silence by saying he'd "sooner be caught with an illegal whiskey still than have anything to do with a dead whooping crane."

In the spring of 1962, the flock of thirty-eight migrated normally, but were met by cold, wet weather in Canada. The Canadian Wildlife Service surveyed the nesting grounds and found that high water had drowned out most of the small grass islands on which the cranes are in the habit of building their nests. It predicted a poor nesting season. This was borne out in November when the flock returned. For only the second time in twenty-five years they came down from the north without a single young bird. To make matters worse, six adults had been lost and the flock was back to thirty-two birds.

The aviculturists seized upon this disaster to prod the bureau on the subject of capturing cranes. John A. Griswold, Curator of Birds at the Philadelphia Zoo, was reported by the Philadelphia *Inquirer* on December 30, 1962, to have said that the "tiny population of whooping cranes is inevitably yet needlessly doomed to extinction in its natural environment.

"There is no doubt about it," the paper quoted him, "the small population is bound to die if man doesn't breed them in captivity. The Fish and Wildlife people are well aware of it, but they're sort of namby-pamby because if something went wrong they'd get it in the neck. . . . Birds raised in captivity won't ever be able to return to the natural state, but at least people will be able to see what they look like."

The words "inevitably yet needlessly doomed to extinction in its natural environment" were more nearly exact than perhaps even Mr. Griswold was aware. At the time he spoke, the whooping cranes were suddenly beset by added danger at Aransas. That autumn they had become innocent bystanders at the Cuban crisis. With the coming of the war threat, the air force began to drop powerful live bombs on their range on Matagorda. The refuge manager, Huyson Johnson, reported the fact to Washington. "Whatever they are using really rattled the windows for twenty miles around," he wrote in his report of December 31, 1962. "While they did not bomb every day, this activity put a lid on our census flights into the restricted area without a mess of red tape. No whoopers were using Matagorda . . . however a potential danger did (and does) exist."

At the same time food conditions on the marsh were poor. In his next report Johnson told how the birds, "unhappy over conditions on their habitat moved restlessly about. Live bombing of Matagorda added chaos to the confusion."

At length Johnson concluded that three whooping cranes were missing, then four. He visited the air-force officer in local command and was provided with a helicopter to search the refuge and the bomb range, but no white corpses were found. The bureau then assigned Erwin Boeker, the biologist who, with Erickson, had been studying the crane problem, to make a further search for the missing whoopers. Boeker reported:

"On December 4, 1962, when bombing commenced, ten whoopers were utilizing Matagorda . . . the number remained constant through February in spite of the bombing. Thus, there is no direct evidence available to indicate that the bombing program adversely affected whooper behavior, or that it was instrumental in causing the disappearance of four of the birds.

"Intensive aerial search over the bombing range failed to disclose any carcasses. On the other hand, the bombing did create a hazardous condition and, along with other human activities, may have contributed to the general unrest of the wintering population. Rather than point at any one disturbing factor on or near the whooping crane wintering grounds as being the responsible factor for creating discontent, it appears we should take a long, hard look at the entire situation.

"At almost any hour of the day or night the area is a beehive of human activity ranging from oyster dredges to SAC bombers. A constant stream of boat and barge traffic moves through the Intercoastal Canal and oil exploration and drilling continue to increase in waters near the Refuge. The question is, how much disturbance can the whooping crane tolerate without creating obscure psychological effects which eventually will cause the entire population to scatter and disappear? Perhaps this point has been reached.

"Another factor that should be considered in connection with the disappearance of four whoopers is a possible shortage of food. Last fall the whoopers made more use of the Refuge interior than usual. This suggests that marine organisms were not abundant even before a series of northers lowered water levels drastically. Supplemental food in the form of wheat and hegari was dropped during this period.

"The fate of the four missing whoopers will probably never be known unless they moved to some undisclosed area last winter and will return to the known wintering grounds this fall. As previously stated, there is no evidence that they were lost due to the bombing program on Matagorda. Yet this activity as well as others on the wintering grounds must be curtailed if the whoopers are to receive sanctuary and maximum safety."

At the time of which Boeker wrote, bombing was certainly not the only danger at Aransas. In February, Shell Oil, drilling just offshore, began to discharge sludge directly into the bay. It continued to do so for ten days before complaints stopped the pollution. Poachers were common on the marshes, where there was no regular patrol. On the Waterway the sign warning approaching boatmen that they were entering a protected area had been blown away by the hurricane two years before and had not been replaced because the necessary funds had not been authorized by the Bureau's Regional Office.

In May the last of the twenty-eight cranes that had somehow survived the perils of the refuge flew north. On May 22 the manager wrote: "No cranes on the Refuge . . . this closes the book on the whooping crane season of '62–'63 with an indicated loss of six birds during the summer of 1962, no young reared and a loss of four on the wintering grounds."

Summer was kinder to them than the almost disastrous winter. The flock lost only two of its number, and triumphantly added seven young for a total of thirty-three birds in the autumn of 1963. As an indication of their symbolic, if not their real, status in American life they were welcomed home by Secretary of the Interior Stewart Udall, who issued a statement announcing the arrival of the whooping cranes at Aransas that November. The secretary said, "The good news on the flock's growth is heartening evidence that thoughtful men can help undo the ravages of thoughtlessness." Perhaps he should have added a line giving equal credit to the tenacity of whooping cranes.

Whooping cranes are caught as they take to the air at Aransas. In flight they show the full beauty of their black-tipped wings.

19

A *sine qua non* of breeding birds in captivity is an ability to distinguish between the sexes. As time wore on and the young birds at the Audubon Park Zoo still refused to declare themselves, the puzzle of their gender became more and more exasperating to all concerned. Whenever the young cranes were penned together, or even adjacent, as a prelude to possible mating, they showed nothing but hostility. It was impossible to tell whether their behavior stemmed from their unnatural circumstances, their immaturity, or the inherently difficult disposition of whooping cranes. There was also the unlikely but dismaying possibility that they were all of the same sex. Of course, the whooping-crane circle not only hoped that a mated pair could be found among the four young but also that one of them would turn out to be of the opposite sex from San Antonio Rosie, whatever that might be. However, whenever anyone suggested to Douglass that he send one of his young birds to San Antonio on a trial basis, he invariably replied that being ignorant of their sex he couldn't know which one to send but that Rosie would be welcome at the New Orleans Zoo anytime the bureau chose to send her to him.

Finally, in 1961, when George and Georgette were four years old, the bureau could stand the frustration—and the prodding of the Whooping Crane Conservation Association—no longer, and assigned a biologist to study the problem of sex determination in whooping cranes.

The biologist chosen, a tall, dark-haired woman with a soft Georgia voice, named Mrs. Roxie Laybourne, discovered that a colleague at Johns Hopkins was facing a similar problem with penguins. In both birds the distinguishing features are hidden within the cloaca of the bird and, at that time, could be identified only by autopsy. Mrs. Laybourne and her friend designed an instrument, which they called a cloacascope, that enabled them to take an enlightening look without damaging a live bird.

In 1960 the bureau had opened a shooting season on sandhill cranes in Texas and New Mexico—a move that greatly dismayed the National Audubon Society, but incidentally provided Mrs. Laybourne with a supply of subjects on which to practice. She visited the refuges where shooting was taking place, and as hunters brought dead cranes to a bureau checking station Mrs. Laybourne examined them and then verified her guess by autopsy. She then moved on to working with live sandhills at the Washington Zoo. When handling live subjects she taped their legs, tarsus to tibia (as though hand-to-shoulder in a human), taped the bill closed, and enveloped the bird's wings in a crane jacket of her own design, made of Canton flannel and closed down the front with a zipper.

By November, 1962, she was satisfied that her method was reliable and did no physical or psychological harm to the birds. The sandhill cranes, she found, recovered their aplomb quite rapidly after the experience.

In the spring of 1962 Mrs. Laybourne packed her crane jacket and cloacascope and journeyed south, hoping to determine the sex of the young whooping cranes at New Orleans and of Rosie at San Antonio. At Audubon Park she found that Douglass was not at the office. He had, however, left word that he would be unable to see her and that she was on no account to lay hands on his cranes. Mrs. Laybourne went on to San Antonio. She examined Rosie and found her to be a female.

The reason Douglass later gave for not allowing Mrs. Laybourne to examine the young cranes was his fear that she might damage them in some way. He had also, of course, kept intact his reasons against sending any young to San Antonio, but at the same time condemned himself to continued suspense. In this dilemma he turned for advice to a man who worked for the Purina Chow Company and from whom he purchased the Game Bird Crumbles and Purina Checkerettes that were part of the cranes' diet.

The Purina Company maintains a laboratory at St. Louis where it does avicultural research. The company offered Douglass the aid of its experts, and Douglass's friend told him that if he could get sandhills to practice on, as Mrs. Laybourne had, he might be able to duplicate her method of sexing whoopers. Sandhills cannot be captured except by permit, so Douglass asked the bureau to provide him with some sandhills. Understandably, the request was refused.

That spring of 1962, Josephine began to lay in early March. Of her first clutch one egg was infertile, but the other hatched on April 8. By April 12 Douglass had realized that the chick had a defect of its right leg. He decided to entrust it to the Purina Company. The chick was flown to the laboratory in St. Louis and a veterinary there operated to correct a slipped tendon. The original operation was a success, but the stitch tore out. The bird was given anesthetic for a second time, and died on the operating table. It was ten days old. In May, Josephine laid a second clutch. Both eggs were taken from the nest and sent to the Purina Laboratory for incubation. Neither hatched, but it was found that both had been fertile. There was, of course, no way to tell if the trip to

St. Louis and the method of incubation had caused the death of the embryos, or if it would have occurred in any case.

Finally, at the end of May, Josephine made a third attempt to raise young whoopers, and for a time it seemed as though she might succeed. On June 25 a young crane was hatched, but lived only a week. It was found dead in the yard of causes that were not determined or recorded. The day before its death Crip broke the remaining egg in the nest. It contained a dead chick.

As word of the spring debacle at New Orleans reached the whooping-crane circle there was mounting chagrin. Dr. Ripley, for one, decided to make a new attempt to free Josephine and Crip. Going over the bureau's head, he wrote a strong letter to the Assistant Secretary of the Interior, Frank Briggs. He told Briggs that the situation of the five captive whooping cranes at New Orleans was a travesty. Scientists all over the world were distressed by the critical situation of *Grus americana*, Ripley wrote, and it was both distressing and embarrassing that the United States Government was, in truth, doing very little to prevent the extinction of the species.

To this the Assistant Secretary politely reiterated the Solicitor's opinion that Josephine and her offspring belonged to the New Orleans Zoo; an attempt to take the birds from Douglass would forestall any chance of the bureau's getting young birds from him voluntarily. He had, he said, been informed that Mr. Douglass would give up a young bird when he had a mated pair in addition to Crip and Josephine. Dr. Ripley was neither satisfied nor convinced. Like some other indignant bystanders, he felt that the Solicitor's opinion was legal mumbo jumbo with which the bureau had allowed itself to become burdened. Since Ripley is a man not easily quenched, he wrote Assistant Secretary Briggs a second letter, again urging legal steps to take Josephine and Crip from Douglass, describing him as a man who, "for one reason or another, seems to have taken extraordinary pains to jeopardize the future of the species in captivity."

Possibly Dr. Ripley's letter spurred the bureau to greater efforts, for in the following spring it was happy to inform Dr. Ripley and other members of the Whooping Crane Advisory Group that it had at last made progress at New Orleans. Douglass had agreed to surrender Josephine's first set of eggs to the bureau, and the bureau had selected William Huey, an aviculturist employed by the New Mexico Department of Fish and Game, to stand by, ready to hatch them.

The spring laying season was awaited with more than usual anticipation. On March 12, 1963, Josephine laid an egg. She pecked a hole in it the same day. In succeeding weeks she laid a second and a third, and as promptly destroyed them. Finally, in April, she laid an egg that was snatched from beneath her before she could break it, and delivered to Mr. Huey in Sante Fe, New Mexico. While this prize was being incubated there, Josephine laid four more eggs; but of these, two were infertile and two were broken before they could be taken from the nest.

The new spirit of cooperation between Douglass and the bureau was destined to be brief. The very week that Douglass relinquished an egg to Mr. Huey, *Life* magazine published a full-page photograph of Douglass dolefully staring at the broken shards of Josephine's first three eggs. The accompanying text stated that out of thirty-four eggs laid by Josephine, thirteen had hatched but that only four chicks had survived. To Douglass the story seemed to imply criticism of his management, and he became highly incensed. He telephoned the bureau and accused it of being instrumental in bringing about this unfavorable publicity. All deals were off, Douglass angrily declared, and the bureau could expect no more whooping-crane eggs from him.

To make this rupture unhappier still, the egg Huey incubated in Sante Fe turned out to be infertile.

Word of the bureau's latest reverse soon reached the Whooping Crane Conservation Association. Its president was now a man named Jack Kiracoff, a hobbyist who had been breeding birds, particularly waterfowl, for many years. Kiracoff mulled over the problem of how relations between Douglass and the bureau might be restored. Kiracoff's proposed solution produced one of the stranger episodes in whooping-crane history. He suggested that the International Wild Waterfowl Association, originally the parent of the Whooping Crane Conservation Association, present Douglass with an award for his "outstanding contributions to aviculture." In view of the fact that a recent meeting of the IWWA had roundly condemned Douglass as a hindrance to the propagation of the whooping crane, some of Kiracoff's confrères were a bit doubtful of the wisdom of the stratagem, but it was decided to give it a try.

Douglass was invited to come to the IWWA's annual convention in October, 1963, to receive the award. He accepted with pleasure. Then, on the day the presentation was to take place, there was a hitch of a bizarre nature. Members of the association were assembled in the hall when word came that Douglass had been robbed. He had lost not only his money but his clothes, and was thus unable to leave his room.

A hastily formed subcommittee sped to the motel to take the imprisoned zoo keeper's measurements. On the way, someone remarked that this was the first time George Douglass had ever been restrained by modesty, but otherwise old enmities were generously put aside. The delegation quickly bought and delivered to Douglass a suitable ensemble.

This strange episode helped to lessen whatever strain might otherwise have existed between Douglass and his hosts. The award was given in a glow of mutual cordiality. Kiracoff felt that his scheme had indeed served its purpose when, shortly afterward, Douglass renewed his offer to give some of Josephine's eggs to the bureau in the coming year.

To prepare for further efforts to raise young whoopers from Josephine's eggs, the bureau hired a full-time aviculturist, a young man named C. Eugene Knoder. Because the bureau still possessed no suitable laboratory of its own it was decided that the eggs would be incubated at the bureau's Lafayette, Louisiana, Research Station, where John Lynch would make available his private avicultural facilities. On March 28 and March 31, 1964, Josephine performed her annual miracle. Knoder was standing by, ready to take the eggs. They were moved in heated, padded boxes to Lafayette, where John Lynch had been conditioning silky bantam hens, weighing only a pound each, to brood half-pound whooping-crane eggs; a trick performed by artfully substituting bigger and bigger eggs for the bantam's own clutch.

The hens, whom Lynch had named Patience and Petulance, did their duty, but once again lack of experience in dealing with whooping cranes brought failure. The first chick was premature because the aviculturists had not realized that the egg should be cooled for periods during incubation. The chick died when it was thirty hours old. The second egg hatched a chick that appeared viable, although it had a defective leg muscle. When it was six days old, Lynch and Knoder decided to move it to the Monte Vista Research Station in Colorado. It died there of a hemorrhage of the ischiadic vein at the age of eighteen days.

Josephine, meanwhile, continued to lay. She broke all records by laying a total of ten eggs. She broke one of them by pecking a hole in it. The others were taken from her and put in the zoo's incubator, but all of them were infertile.

By now there was more than ever reason to fear that Josephine or Crip, or perhaps both of them, were too old to produce viable young, and it was more than ever important that Rosie—now, at last, known to be a female—have an opportunity to do her share. It also occurred to the bureau that Rosie might perform a further service. If she were exposed to the young birds at New Orleans, any that were hostile to her might be presumed to be female, and any that were friendly might be male.

Therefore in April, 1964, the bureau decided to accept Douglass's offer and move Rosie to New Orleans. Before sending her, the bureau took the precaution of obtaining a firm legal agreement that any offspring from her would be the property of the Federal Government.

At Aransas the winter months of 1963–1964 were more peaceful for the wild whooping cranes than they had been the year before. The wild acorn crop was good, and the birds were also fed with grain. The air force ceased using live bombs. The only untoward event was the discovery, in March, of the scattered remains of a whooping crane on Bludworth Island, just off the refuge. The corpse, found only a hundred yards from the canal, was of an immature bird, one of the twins of a family that had only a single parent. The loss reduced the flock to thirty-two, all of whom migrated normally in the spring.

In early summer the Canadian Wildlife Service predicted an unusually good season. From the air its biologist, Nicholas S. Novakowski, saw four breeding pairs of cranes. By June, one pair had hatched a single young bird and two pairs had twins.

For the rest of the summer Novakowski made only occasional flights, for fear of disturbing the nestlings, but in September he flew low in a helicopter for a thorough look. As he passed over the spot where he had seen a pair of twins, Novakowski saw only one young bird, and it seemed to be in trouble; its right wing dangled and it tripped over the primary feathers every few steps. Novakowski asked the pilot to bring the helicopter down low for a closer look, but the adults dashed at the plane with flapping wings, and the pilot was barely able to veer and rise quickly enough to avoid them. Novakowski flew back to Fort Smith with all possible speed and wired his discovery to the two Wildlife services. Within a few hours he had been instructed to capture the injured bird.

The next day, with an assistant, Novakowski returned to the nesting area. The youngster was spotted next to a dry lake where, fortunately, the helicopter was able to land. The men chased the young bird through the brush until it tripped and fell. Then they caught it easily. It was surprisingly unresistant as it was wrapped in sacking and put in a cage tied to the outside of the helicopter. At Fort Smith the bird was put aboard a commercial flight to Edmonton, where it was immediately taken to a local veterinary clinic. An X ray showed that the injured wing was partially dislocated and that a two-inch sliver of charred wood had pierced the bird's breast muscle. Probably the youngster had flown against a burnt tree and impaled itself on a branch while learning to fly. To the surprise of its captors the young bird seemed quite unafraid as it was handled, and readily accepted a meal of minced egg, mealworms, hamburger, and fresh smelts.

That afternoon Eugene Knoder, the avicultural expert the bureau had hired to handle Josephine's eggs, arrived by plane to take the little crane, nestled in a cardboard box, to Monte Vista. The trip was interrupted by a stop at Cutbank, Montana. Here Knoder took the crane out of the carton for exercise. A crowd gathered, but the bird walked up and down the cement apron quite unconcerned, eating and drinking as though it were already used to people. Knoder came to wonder if perhaps at this stage of their lives young whoopers assume people are other birds and learn to fear humans only when their parents teach them to, during migration and on the wintering ground.

For the first two weeks at Monte Vista, the young whooper, now named Lady Bird, did well, and then, without warning, became very ill. One morning it was barely able to stand. As the day passed it refused to eat or drink, and seemed near death. Knoder sent for all the medical help he could gather. Four veterinarians arrived and administered a barrage of medicines. The bird responded, and within a day made a remarkable recovery, only to get in trouble again.

The young crane was penned indoors at night. In the morning it customarily celebrated its release by flapping its wings and running about. One morning, during these capers, it caught one toe in the bandage on its wing, and fell, breaking the already injured wing in two places. Again veterinarians went to work and repaired the damage, and again the whooper recovered. It was soon strong enough for a session with Mrs. Laybourne, who pronounced it a male. The name Lyndon Bird was rejected by officials mindful of their responsibility for dignity, and Lady Bird became "Canus," a blend of "Canada" and "U.S."

20

Since the cranes came back to Aransas in the autumn of 1964, a number of things have happened that, joined to all that has gone before, will play a part in determining how many more journeys lie ahead of them. Will it be ten, twenty, fifty, or will they fly for many generations more? Some signs point toward a renewed future for them. Some indicate that the wild birds do not, indeed, have far to go.

As the returning cranes were counted in November, 1964, it became clear they had again brought off one of their astonishing feats of last-ditch recovery. Not only did every one of the thirty-two birds that went north in the spring come back to Aransas, but the flock brought with them ten young birds—eight singles and one pair of twins. Including Canus, they had produced the record-breaking count of eleven young. The wild flock was thus forty-two. With eight cranes in captivity, the birds had at last reached that number whose roundness seems to give it some magic meaning: there were fifty whooping cranes on earth.

Meanwhile, there was another event that, taken purely from the point of view of the whooping cranes, was bound to be influential. On November 10, 1964, George Douglass died. He was fifty-seven years old. His obituary, carried throughout the nation by The Associated Press, identified him as the only man ever to raise whooping cranes in captivity—a fact that is indisputable, but double-edged. Taken either way, it will no doubt win him a place in the ornithological annals of the future. It is possible to guess, too, that the whooping cranes brought him some of his life's most glowing moments of satisfaction—and that there were other moments when he wished he had never heard the words *Grus americana.*

The New Orleans Park Commission filled Douglass's vacant post by appointing one of its number, a retired businessman named William Pohlmann, whose experience in breeding horses had led him to an interest in the zoo.

Pohlmann responded cordially to overtures from the Bureau of Sport Fisheries and Wildlife. He welcomed Mrs. Laybourne and Eugene Knoder to the zoo. Mrs. Laybourne made the important discovery that

George, Georgette, and Pepper are males. Peewee, the third chick, who was born in 1958, is a female.

Mr. Pohlmann accepted an arrangement whereby new quarters for the cranes would be constructed at the expense of the bureau and Eugene Knoder would supervise future nestings. The bureau assured Pohlmann that it had no desire to move any of the present flock from New Orleans but that future offspring should be distributed "elsewhere" to guard against such catastrophes as disease, hurricane, fire, or flood. All the offspring of Rosie and half of the young of Peewee, should there be any, are to be federal property.

During the winter of 1964–1965, Knoder went to New Orleans several times. He found that Leo Buras, the diffident, soft-spoken keeper, had already successfully matched Rosie and George. Buras had always believed Peewee to be a female. Now, with Knoder's approval, he penned her with her brother, the former Georgette, renamed George II. For a time the two seemed to get along quite well, and even to be starting a courtship. Then, suddenly, an antagonism developed, and they had to be separated. It is not uncommon in wild birds to have a sort of "false pairing," or partial ceremony that is suddenly ended, only to be taken up again later; so there is still hope that Peewee will in time accept a mate.

The new pens built during the winter are roofed with wire mesh at a height of ten feet, which allows room for the leaps of the courting cranes, and are fifty feet on each side. There are bamboo curtains to give the birds privacy. In contrast to the weeds and dust that floored the old pens, there is now a ground cover of bluegrass and clover. The old tin water basins are gone. Water flows continuously into concrete pools in each pen.

However, in spite of all the promise of the courtship dances and the improved accommodations, the spring of 1965 brought forth no young whooping cranes. Rosie and George mated, but they did not go so far as to build a nest. Only Josephine, that steady old grande dame, did her part, but less generously than in previous years. She laid two eggs that were taken from her and put under silky bantams provided by John Lynch, but both eggs were infertile. On May 13 she laid a third egg, which Lynch picked up and brought to Knoder for incubation at the Monte Vista laboratory. When it failed to hatch, Knoder opened it and found that the chick had died in the shell two days before hatching. Josephine did not lay again.

The previous fall there had been another important change in the cast of characters managing the cranes' future. Daniel Janzen, who had been the Director of the Bureau of Sport Fisheries and Wildlife since its formation seven years earlier, retired, and his place was taken by

John S. Gottschalk, who had been Northeast Regional Director at Boston since 1959.

The job of director of the bureau is one that comes with limitations and frustrations firmly attached. The bureau's purse strings are tightly tied by Congress. Each dime that is appropriated is earmarked by Congress for a specified purpose, and may be spent for no other. Thus Congress effectively controls the bureau's actions. In the past, Congress has been greatly influenced by the views of the sportsmen's lobbies who watch jealously to see that the bureau's major expenditures are to promote "sport," and not such frivolities as wild creatures in general or even whooping cranes in particular. In spite of these financial limitations, there are many things the bureau director can do for the whooping cranes if he chooses, beginning with a willingness to consider their existence a matter of importance. Mr. Gottschalk quite quickly convinced the whooping-crane circle that his administration would have the cranes very much in mind.

Recently, at Aransas, there have been changes helpful to the cranes. Some of these were already under way during Janzen's regime, but Gottschalk plans not only to maintain but to add to improvements made in the cranes' behalf.

For example, in the autumn of 1964 the cranes arrived to find a ninety-acre plot of land fenced to keep out four-footed intruders, and seeded with grain crops. The whoopers came down off their high horses long enough to join hundreds of sandhills at the feast. As long as the grain held out, the cranes seldom wandered off the refuge. In 1965, the fenced area was doubled and planted with crops designed to last longer into the winter. In addition the manager was instructed to keep tabs on the marine food available. If it fails he will supply grain to tide the whoopers over a barren spell.

Recently steps have been taken to protect the cranes from people. There is a better patrol of the Waterway, and, as a small but important improvement, the warning signs have been replaced. At last there has been an effort to stop the harassment of whooping cranes by low-flying aircraft. Texas is the land of the private airplane and, in recent years, more and more airborne cowboys have buzzed the refuge. In 1965, the refuge manager wrote to the Federal Aviation Agency about the problem. The agency replied that the refuge could be put in the "restricted" category only if the birds were a danger to aircraft, not vice versa. However, the agency promised to warn pilots that there is a five-hundred-foot ceiling over the refuge.

The air force, of course, continued to use the Matagorda Range during the winter of 1964–1965, but not with live ammunition. The thought has been wistfully expressed that there are other places available to the air force for bombing practice, but no place for the whooping cranes to winter except at Aransas, but it is probably too much to hope that the air force will ever close the range and move away.

If one asks why these protective steps, all simple in themselves, were not taken when Robert Allen suggested them more than ten years ago, the primary answer is, of course, "money." The annual budget for all the Wildlife refuges—there are 280 and they cover 17,000,000 acres—is $13,000,000. This is a tenth of the sum allowed the Park Department. Bureau officials sadly attribute the difference to the fact that the Parks serve people directly, and are thus vote-getters. Wildlife refuges, when they are doing their job best, keep people out of land reserved for the use of animals. To the public and its legislators the bureau's function often seems restrictive and negative.

Nevertheless, money is now being spent on the whooping cranes that wasn't being spent before. Veterans of the wildlife wars will say that the cranes are among the beneficiaries of a new trend that has only just begun to assert itself. It is becoming more and more apparent that great numbers of Americans are interested in conservation in a broad sense, and not just for a purpose as limited as "recreation" or "sport." As one old-timer within the bureau recently explained, "Popular demand, expressed through Congress, is what makes us tick. In the past we have been serving two forceful groups: sportsmen and farmers. We are partly financed by the fees collected from hunters. The idea of considering creatures other than waterfowl is new to us because in the past all other programs were unimportant to the people who supplied our funds."

At this late date there is a limit to what can be done at Aransas. In its efforts to improve the habitat of the cranes, the bureau recently met a serious defeat of the old-fashioned purse-and-politics variety. Ever since Robert Allen's day it has been clear that the wintering cranes need more land; particularly if their numbers should increase. But the bureau is one of the few federal agencies that is tied hand and foot in acquiring land.

The bureau is permitted to buy land for a refuge only after the legislature and governor of the state concerned have consented to the purchase. Adjacent to Aransas is a tract of five thousand acres, the Tatten Ranch, whose owners would willingly sell it to the bureau. In 1965, the bureau decided that, although the asking price of $1,100,000 is twenty times the per-acre price paid for Aransas thirty years ago, the tract should be added to the refuge. However, when the bureau consulted with local politicians, a group called the County Commissioners, these men refused to recommend the purchase to the governor because it would remove a large proportion of county land from the tax rolls. Meanwhile, the House Appropriations Committee of the Eighty-ninth Congress, appraising the Department of the Interior's request for funds in 1965, took an equally dim view of the proposal. In the words of a member of the committee,

"It is not evident to the Committee why an additional five thousand acres should be acquired at a cost of $1,100,000 to provide nesting and breeding habitat for about thirty-two whooping cranes when the Federal Government already owns 47,000 acres for this purpose." Thus, with casual inaccuracy, the committee destroyed what may have been the cranes' last chance for an adequate winter home at Aransas.

The hazards of oil pollution of the surrounding water, and drilling on the refuge, are economic facts of life that the bureau must get along with as best it can, but much depends on the vigilance and persuasiveness of bureau officials as they keep an eye on these activities. Meanwhile, the State of Texas, which has not shown itself notably interested in protecting the cranes, has projects in the works that may have widespread and lethal effects not only on the cranes but also on a vast segment of the nation's wildlife resources. The first of these is called the Texas Basins Project, and envisions an irrigation canal running along the rim of the gulf, a few miles inland, that would carry the waters of the Sabine and Trinity rivers, which now flow into the gulf near the Louisiana border, as far south as Brownsville on the Mexican border. Since this ditch would cut across every river, creek, and rivulet that now runs into the gulf between these two points, six hundred miles apart, it could prevent any flow of fresh water from reaching the shore.

The complex marine life along the gulf shores depends on runoff from the land freshening waters that are otherwise too saline. Unless arrangements can be made to let sufficient fresh water cross the ditch and reach the gulf, the effect on marine life, and hence all wildlife, will be enormous to an unpredictable degree. In addition, there is the unforeseeable effect of the dams and irrigation systems that have been proposed for the whole river system of the interior of Texas. What will be the result of the pollution, wherever inland waters finally reach the gulf, from the tons of pesticides that will be used on the new farmlands? Marine creatures, blue crabs, for instance, and shellfish, are highly sensitive to such chemicals. The water "development" project of Texas is of such staggering size and complexity that no one can foresee the outcome. The Bureau of Sport Fisheries and Wildlife has already mentioned the existence of Aransas and its precious tenants to the planners in the Interior Department's Bureau of Reclamation, and they have promised to "allow" fresh water to flow into the vicinity of the refuge; but what will actually happen if all these projects come about cannot be accurately predicted by anyone.

All water bottoms along the Gulf Coast of Texas and, hence, around the Aransas Refuge, are owned by the State of Texas. Just beneath the surface of the water is a vast store of wealth in the form of oyster reefs whose shells can be dredged up and pulverized for use in various forms of construction. These oyster reefs form shallows that are the nurseries for the fish, shrimp, crabs, weeds, and other marine life of the shore upon which birds and countless other creatures depend. Until recently shell dredging was not permitted closer than 1,300 feet from land. In 1963, Texas reorganized its Conservation Department and placed power in the hands of a three-man commission whose first act was to delight the shell dredgers of Texas by changing the offshore limit from 1,300 to 300 feet, an act that outraged conservationists. Having pried open the treasure chest, the commissioners are busily leasing oyster reefs to dredgers who may, if not stopped, destroy the marine life of the gulf shoreline so rapidly that by the time the canal and dam builders arrive to change the face of nature there will be nothing left in the area for conservationists to worry about. The Texas commissioners have already leased reefs in St. Charles Bay, and while this is not whooping-crane territory, it is too close to the refuge for comfort. The Bureau of Sport Fisheries and Wildlife has protested, but without effect.

For a final item in the catalogue of large-scale hazards to whooping cranes, we move to the Far North and the problems created by the whooper's smaller cousins, the sandhill cranes. These are social birds that fly in flocks and feed together in grainfields. Thousands of sandhills nest in Canada and Alaska. As the flocks of sandhills come down from the north, they pass over the wheat provinces at the very moment that the farmers are harvesting. The mowed grain lies on the ground in great smooth swaths. When flocks of sandhills descend on the fields they not only eat greedily but also kick the grain into disorderly heaps. As a result, many Saskatchewan farmers, and farmers in the wheat areas of the northern United States, would like to see an end to all cranes.

Legal crane hunting in the United States and Canada ended by treaty in 1915. For many years the Canadian Fish and Wildlife Service handled the complaints of farmers on an individual basis, by issuing a shooting permit to any farmer who could show he was suffering a cash loss. Lately both the farmers and the powerful sportsmen's organizations have clamored for an open season on sandhills. The Canadian Service resisted. One reason for its reluctance was that any crane shooting would obviously endanger the whooping cranes migrating in the same region and sometimes in the company of sandhills. The young whoopers, not yet much bigger than sandhills, and disguised by their russet feathers, would be in particular peril.

However, by 1964 the depredations of the sandhills, the wrath of the farmers, and the pressure of the sportsmen had reached such proportions that the Canadian Service gave in and opened a sandhill season in Saskatchewan that fall. The service added the assurance that whooping cranes would be protected by wardens who would patrol hunting areas, and if a dead whooper were found the season would be promptly closed. The United States Bureau, which must agree to all regulations affecting migratory birds, made no objections. It was hardly in a position to, since, at the request both of the Canadians and of our own sportsmen, it had already opened a season on the shooting of sandhills in Arizona and New Mexico. Again, the National Audubon Society protested heatedly and futilely. It pointed out that the best way to stop the sandhills from damaging farmers is to provide refuges and food to draw the birds away from croplands. The society objected that the proposed safeguards to whooping cranes were patently ineffectual; furthermore, if the Canadian Service has enough wardens to inspect every hunter's gamebag, these wardens would be better employed flushing the sandhills out of the wheat fields, thus solving the depredation problem without gunfire.

In 1964 and in 1965, sandhill cranes were legally shot in Saskatchewan. Game wardens did not report sighting any whooping cranes in the shooting areas, but the distances that they scanned by plane are tremendous, and hunters who accidentally shoot whoopers are not likely to publicize their luck. There is thus far no proof that sandhill shooting has killed any whooping cranes, but it is hard to imagine how it can fail to do so eventually. And, of course, as with any wall that has been breached, it is far easier to open a shooting season than it is to close it.

21

The catalogue of dangers to the whooping crane is, of course, simply a selection from the catalogue of what are called the "pressures" of our changing times. Fortunately, not all the pressures on that long list are inimical to wildlife. Something that might be called a "counterpressure" offers hope for wildlife: a trend toward conservation as a popular cause. More and more legislators in Washington, hearing a new murmur in the American heartbeat, realize that bird-watchers have a vote. In this connection a hitherto unheralded champion of the whooping crane recently came onstage in the person of Senator Karl E. Mundt of South Dakota.

Senator Mundt, who is no more unlikely in the cast of the whooping-crane drama than some others who have played a role, once served on the Fish and Game Commission of his state and was national vice-president of the Izaak Walton League. In Congress he has shown a continued interest in wildlife. His hobbies are hunting and fishing. His state is on the whooping-crane flyway. When the fate of the whooping cranes cropped up in Congress in 1962, it was Senator Mundt who lent them a hand. At that time the question of the funds the bureau needed in order to make studies of sandhills as a preliminary to whooping-crane propagation came before the Senate Appropriations subcommittee. The House subcommittee had cut out the appropriation. Senator Mundt insisted it be restored, and so, thanks to him, the bureau was able to go on with these crucial experiments. Perhaps as an example of the rule of human nature that says a man who has done someone a good turn is all the more devoted to the recipient of the favor, Senator Mundt has been a faithful friend of the cranes ever since. Recently the bureau needed that friendship very much.

For the past three or four years the bureau has been working on a program that only a short time ago would not have had a chance of finding congressional support. In November, 1964, Secretary Udall announced that the Bureau of Sport Fisheries and Wildlife wished to embark upon a project of research and protection designed to save from extinction a number of species of birds and mammals that are now in danger. He proposed a new laboratory at the Patuxent Wildlife Research Center in Maryland, including avicultural facilities to house the sandhill cranes that are the pilot project for whooping-crane propagation. In April, 1965, Senator Mundt pushed through an amendment to an appropriations bill that allotted the bureau $35,000 to start the work. The buildings and staff were ready in early 1966. The initial sum is not large, but the start of the "Rare and Endangered Project" is tremendously significant not just for the whoopers but also as official recognition of a new attitude toward wildlife. The project, which is directed by Dr. Erickson, is the first in which creatures have been chosen for study because of their imperiled position rather than their economic value, and the Patuxent Center is the first research facility ever devoted to such an idealistic purpose. High on the list beside the whooping crane are the California condor, the black-footed ferret, the ivory-billed woodpecker (if in fact any still exist), and there will be no lack of additional candidates.

The groundwork for whooping-crane studies at Patuxent was laid by the work with sandhills begun by Erwin Boeker in 1961. The first phase was an effort to find out if it is possible to get a breeding stock of sandhills either by trapping wild birds or by taking eggs from the nests of wild birds and incubating them artificially: an experiment with obvious implications in the whooping-crane controversy. Boeker experimented with three groups: greater and lesser sandhills trapped in the wild, and greater sandhills hatched from eggs stolen from the nests of wild birds. None of the methods of trapping worked out satisfactorily. "Walk-in" traps were unreliable and unselective; footsnares were ineffective; nets shot from cannons caused many injuries. The second stage of the sandhill experiment compared the survival of the different groups in captivity. The birds caught as yearlings remained wild and were difficult to handle; a number were killed in the same sort of unpredictable accidents that have so often attended the handling of whooping cranes. Hand-reared greater sandhills, on the other hand, did much better. Some were lost in infancy, but all of those that came through this critical period grew into healthy and tractable birds. By the end of 1963 it had been established that it would be far better to rear cranes, whoopers or sandhills by taking their eggs than by attempting to capture them in the wild.

Late in 1963 the bureau at last was given funds to hire Eugene Knoder expressly to carry on the sandhill experiments. There was not, however, enough money for adequate facilities. Knoder's work was done in small and rather makeshift quarters at the bureau's Monte Vista Research Station in Colorado where he was handicapped by the severe climate, inadequate incubators and a lack of trained help. During 1964, Knoder, John Lynch, and others in the bureau concentrated on solving the problems involved in picking up and hatching eggs taken from wild sandhills. The experimenters devised a portable incubator to carry eggs from the nests to the laboratory. It is an elaborate device, electrically powered by batteries, equipped with such refinements as sponges to maintain humidity and foam-rubber mounts to prevent jarring its precious contents. The experimenters compared different methods of incubation and tried out various diets on the growing chicks. In one experiment thirty eggs were collected. Of these, twenty-three hatched, but seven chicks died in their first six months. Each death provided a lesson of one sort or another. One four-month-old crane pecked at a shiny shovel hanging on a rack. The shovel fell and fractured its skull. Needless to say there will be no shovels in future pens.

Meanwhile, Dr. Erickson, and other biologists in the bureau, notably Dr. John W. Aldrich, had been working out a long-range plan to apply the fruits of this research to the whooping cranes. Erickson believes that the odds on the whoopers' survival in the wild are becoming progressively shorter as hazards to them multiply. He points out that despite the goodly number of young cranes brought to Aransas over the years the flock has not increased in due proportion. In the past sixteen years seventy-two youngsters have been counted in Texas, but still the number of adult birds has hovered in the thirties. The flock has indeed increased, but so slowly that the scales could be tilted by the loss of even one productive pair of birds. He is convinced that the flocks' margin of safety is far too narrow; that only a flock numbered in the hundreds can surely survive the ever-increasing array of hostile forces. In Erickson's opinion it is unlikely that such an increase can take place naturally in time to save the cranes. Therefore, he reasons, the additional birds must be bred artificially, under forced draft, with the hope that they can somehow be returned to the wild. This is, of course, in essence, what the aviculturists have urged for ten years. The difference is that ten years ago neither the bureau, nor anyone else, had the skill or the means to accomplish it. It is only now, at last, that the bureau's real interest, expressed in its "Rare and Endangered Project," and supported by proper facilities and competent biologists, gives the venture of captive breeding and release of whooping cranes any chance of success.

In spite of the need for haste, the plan that the bureau proposes cannot be fulfilled overnight. It will probably be ten to fifteen years from the day that the first whooping crane is hatched in this project to the day the first whooping crane can be released. There are two reasons for the long span involved: the length of time required for whooping cranes to mature and breed, and the large number of birds that will be needed for the attempt to return them to the wild. Experience with game birds has shown that they must be released in massive numbers in order to provide sufficient survivors to start a new generation. Thus it will take two or three generations of captive whooping cranes to produce the requisite number of birds for release. The return of the birds to the wild is, of course, the most difficult and mysterious phase, biologically speaking, of the operation. In this, everything will depend on experiments yet to be made with the sandhills now in captivity.

The plan that the bureau proposes has been mapped out in this manner:

Whooping-crane eggs will be picked up from the nesting grounds—stolen from the nests of the cranes—in a summer when a wet-weather cycle seems to have begun. The reason for gearing the egg-taking to wet weather is Dr. Erickson's assumption that young hatched during a wet cycle are less likely to survive their adolescence, and would be lost to the flock in any case.

During the early summer months the Canadian Wildlife Service will survey the nesting grounds and locate the nests. In the second or third week after eggs have been laid a party of Canadian and United States Wildlife Service men will land by helicopter and take a maximum of six eggs. These will be flown to Fort Smith in the portable incubator and thence to Patuxent, where other incubators will await them. To be considered are the pros and cons of taking one egg from each of six nests, leaving the second egg of the clutch, or taking two eggs from each of three nests. In the first instance experience with sandhills indicates that the parents may return and incubate the remaining egg. Furthermore, from a normal clutch of two eggs, one of the chicks is usually lost anyway before the southward migration. On the other hand, if both eggs from each nest are taken, only three, rather than six, pairs of nesting cranes will have been disturbed. The birds that have been robbed may recycle and lay again. In the event that they do so, their chicks would probably not reach flying age in time to escape the autumn cold, but then it might be possible to rescue them by helicopter, as Canus was rescued, and add them to the captive stock.

On the basis of recent crops of young birds, Erickson believes that the flock of wild whoopers now contains at least ten or twelve mated pairs who may produce twenty to twenty-four eggs in a season. The six stolen eggs would thus represent a loss to the flock of perhaps 25 to 30 percent of potential young and probably a smaller fraction of the young that would be likely to appear in the fall at Aransas. This loss, he believes, is even less significant than it seems if one considers the probability that some of these young, hatched during a wet cycle, are destined to die before they can mature and become breeders. He thus reasons that the removal of six eggs will reduce the future productivity of the wild flock very little, if at all. Erickson feels that eggs should be taken each summer as long as the wet cycle continues. Judging by the past, this might be for three or four successive years. By varying the location of pilfered nests, different pairs of birds should provide the eggs each year so that the resulting captives will be as genetically diverse as possible.

What will happen once the bureau is possessed of the precious stolen eggs is, of course, the crux of the matter, and also something on which the bureau, so often jinxed by the cranes, is wary of making predictions. Ideally, however, if the whooping-crane eggs hatch as successfully as the sandhills have, two-thirds of the eighteen stolen eggs in this hypothesis should produce chicks. Of these twelve chicks, eight might be reared to maturity. Since it would be unlikely that luck would provide four of each sex, the eight birds might yield three pairs. Three pairs would not be enough to produce the number of young essential to the program, nor would they give sufficient genetic diversity to a captive flock. Therefore the taking of eggs from the wild would have to be resumed whenever a second wet cycle occurred.

The age of sexual maturity of the whooping crane is still unknown, but it is probably between four and six. If eggs were taken for the first time in the summer of 1967, it is possible that in 1971 or 1972 the cranes hatched from them would begin to reproduce. Young birds are less productive than older birds. In the first season the captives might lay only two to four eggs. Thus the first generation of captive-bred birds would be small, perhaps only a dozen or so. Inevitably accidents and disease would take a toll. However, in the next few years, with the birds maturing and laying up to eight eggs per couple as they hit their reproductive stride, and with the young from eggs gathered in later years maturing also, there would be a surge of productivity. The goal is to have at least ten breeding pairs of birds, as little inbred as possible, who should be able to produce fifty or more young birds in a season. This point, which might be achieved in ten years of breeding, would be the signal to begin the effort to release whooping cranes to the wild.

Up to this point in the program the captive cranes, destined to devote their lives to producing young, would be handled in an ordinary manner; but when it came to releasing the young, very special techniques that have, in truth, never been tested, would have to be employed. The bureau is counting on the sandhill experiments leading the whooper experiments by five years in every aspect and indicating how the release of the whooping cranes may be accomplished. If all goes well the sandhills now in captivity will start to breed at Patuxent in the summer of 1966 or 1967. Within four or five years, enough young may have been produced to allow the start of release experiments. Releasing sandhills under varying conditions may answer such crucial questions as where it is best to release them, at what age, and at what season.

To raise birds of peculiarly mysterious psychology and migratory behavior so that they are equipped with whatever particular knowledge a whooping crane needs in order to function as a whooping crane is obviously a formidable undertaking. It is already well established that birds raised in association with human beings will not succeed if turned loose in the wild. A first requirement, then, is that the young whooping cranes destined for release be raised without human contact. Perhaps they will be in screened pens with food automatically dispensed. Perhaps a system that has worked with Canada geese will work with sandhills and then whoopers. In this instance the parent geese were wing-clipped and kept within a large enclosure. They raised their young in conditions that simulated the wild. When the young matured they joined flocks of wild geese, and migrated normally. Whether this could be done with whooping cranes is something that one can only guess.

For the time being the bureau has left out of its calculations any young that may be raised at New Orleans. In the first place they cannot be counted before they are hatched. A second reason is uncertainty about Josephine's genetic background. Although her young presumably carry the extremely interesting and valuable trait of nonmigratory nesting, there is no way of knowing what else her genes carry that may not be so desirable, particularly for survival in the wild. Erickson and Lynch think it possible that Douglass may have been unjustly blamed for the death of young that were perhaps inherently prone to disease or malformation. For these reasons bureau biologists consider the future of the New Orleans young a separate matter from the stock that will be raised at Patuxent. Possibly later there can be an attempt to inbreed the New Orleans stock to renew a nonmigratory flock; but this is too far ahead for real speculation.

In the spring of 1964 the bureau and the Canadian Wildlife Service jointly announced their plan to take whooping-crane eggs for propagation. The avicultural group was greatly pleased with it, but the proposal was given a guarded reception by the National Audubon Society. They had many questions to ask—particularly on the tricky question of returning the captive whooping cranes to the wild, which they feel must always be the goal of any whooping-crane project. Of the aspects that worried them, one was, of course, how it was to be done; another was *whether* it would be done. It is not impossible to imagine that once a stock of tame whooping cranes is safely established in captivity, a great deal of the pressure "to do something to save the cranes" will be withdrawn. In the minds of those who do not think of the whooping cranes in the way that Robert Allen did, as creatures that must be free to be truly themselves, the species will have been saved. It might then be convenient to skip the final difficult step of returning the birds to the wild. To this the bureau can answer only that it is sincere in its professed purpose of reintroducing the birds. Its present officers believe that the officials in charge when the time comes will honor the commitments, and, presumably there will still be individuals, or such agencies as the National Audubon Society, to remind them of it.

In the spring of 1965, the National Audubon Society decided to add its approval to the bureau's plan for the whooping crane. The society's biologists, Roland Clement and Alexander Sprunt, IV, feel that the plan has now been worked out with a care that not only gives it a reasonable chance of success, but also subjects the wild flock to a minimum of danger. The money appropriated for the bureau's "Rare and Endangered" program at last gives assurance that there will be facilities equal to the job. The bureau has promised that it will not make the critical attempt to take whooping-crane eggs until practice with sandhills at Patuxent has provided an experienced staff, tested equipment and the safest possible techniques. Thus, when the bureau's whooping-crane project begins, possibly in 1967, the National Audubon Society will be among those cheering it on—and for the first time in many years the whole whooping-crane circle will be united.

Now that it is possible to look back on the roles played by various members of that circle, it seems, paradoxically, that all the opponents in the controversy were right. Those who wanted whooping cranes captured were at least correct in their belief that aviculture had something to offer, and it was their pressure that forced the bureau to make a start. The National Audubon Society was equally correct in its conviction that experiments with wild whoopers would have been worse than doing nothing. Its staunch defense of the wild flock prevented any premature meddling with them that would quite likely have been not only useless but fatal. And, finally, the bureau is to be thanked for having at last found a course that offers real hope of saving *Grus americana.*

22

On Thursday, September 9, 1965, a hurricane of extraordinary violence, which the Weather Bureau had named Hurricane Betsy, drove directly upon the city of New Orleans. As the barometer fell, the scene at the zoo was one of frantic battening down and shifting of animals to what, the men there hoped, would be safe quarters in the brick buildings. Oddly, most wild birds and animals become very tractable, almost as in the story of the Ark, when they are faced with natural catastrophe. In birds, hollow bones and body air sacs apparently act as "aneroid barometers," sensitive to outside atmospheric pressure. As pressure begins to drop, birds are at first very nervous, but as it falls to a hurricane low they become almost numb. Thus, Leo Buras with the help of other keepers was able to capture the whooping cranes in their large pens and move them into shelter. Each bird was walked across the grounds with one man holding the bill and a man on each side of it holding it by the wing.

By three thirty in the afternoon, with the wind already rising in the huge live oaks surrounding the park, the whooping cranes were under cover. On Pohlmann's orders the two pairs and the four single birds were put in different areas of the zoo as a precaution against the demolition of any one building. Josephine and Crip found themselves in a corridor, closed by doors at either end, leading to the indoor cage of a giraffe. As the wind rose to the full thunder of hurricane force and trees began to crash, all the zoo's human inhabitants retreated to the Administration Building to spend the night.

The storm abated shortly after midnight. With flashlights the men ventured out to assess the damage, and found they would first have to hack paths through the tangled barriers of fallen trees. (In the end it took fifty men twelve days to clear the debris.) By dawn Friday, after the storm, Pohlmann and the keepers had reached the buildings in which the cranes were confined, and found that all of them had come through safely, as indeed had all the zoo's large animals. The only casualties were a number of small fowl housed in wooden buildings that had been demolished. All the brick buildings were intact, but the once lovely park landscape was a ghastly tangle of roots and branches of fallen trees.

The new crane pens, of sturdy wire mesh, had come through undamaged, and on Friday morning the whooping cranes were all returned to their regular quarters. If any of them were unduly excited by the unusual aspect of things and the crews of men with axes and saws working around them, no one noticed it.

Then, on Sunday, a helicopter hovered over the zoo. The flashing and noise of the whirling rotor blades were too much for the cranes. Several of the birds crouched in alarm and then dashed about their pens. Their whoops could be heard throughout the grounds. Leo Buras came running to quiet them. As he got there, Josephine gathered herself as though for a mighty effort of escape, and, half running, half flying, with all the remaining power of her pinioned wings, hurled herself into the air and hit the fence with the full weight of her hurtling body. It threw her back, but she rose and battered herself against it, until, by the time Leo reached her, her wing bones were rubbed raw. The helicopter moved on, and Josephine became quiet. She seemed not to have suffered any serious injury. The following morning, Monday, September 13, a keeper named Vincent Beals checked the crane pens when he came on duty at six in the morning. All was normal, except in the pen that contained Josephine and Crip. Josephine lay on the ground. Beals entered and picked her up. She was quite dead.

In November, 1965, the refuge manager at Aransas counted the returning cranes and found that again they had had a good year. They had

Whooping cranes join briefly in flight at Aransas. How much longer the great birds will fly no one can now say.

brought the fine crop of eight young birds with them. There were thirty-six adults and so the total was a new high-water mark of forty-four whooping cranes. On the other hand six birds had vanished. One had died when it hit a high wire on the journey south. The fate of the others was as mysterious as ever and, as ever, an irreparable loss.

For some of us there is a strange magic in knowing that once again the flock has completed another extraordinary journey. Somehow, mysteriously, from high in the air the birds sense the nearness beneath them of the small patches of sand and water that are theirs. They brake their flight, and descend, floating down in narrower and narrower spirals. For an instant before a whooping crane touches the ground, its huge wings seem to hold it in the air. Its legs stretch out, reaching for the earth, and then it settles. Its great tapered, shining white body comes down so softly it seems as though it could light upon an egg and not break it. It is a marvelous thing.

Then, the cranes' tall white forms dot the marsh. They hunt for food, guide their young with the low talking notes that so enchanted Robert Allen, and maintain their vigilant watch over their territories. They are, of course, unknowing and unconcerned that this small homeland is all that is left of the once-wide world in which their species was formed.

We might say that if the cranes are lucky they will continue to exist. It would be more accurate to say that if *we* are lucky *Grus americana* will continue to exist. The walls of their last sanctuary are fragile. Strong, perhaps irresistible, forces will continue to press in. As the result of a bureaucratic red pencil, a military decision, or an economic opportunity, the cranes' last redoubt could be taken. In that case the end of the species would not, of course, be sudden or ruthlessly executed. It would merely be a matter of letting nature—the nature of things as they are today—take its course. On the other hand, there is true commitment and growing vigilance among those who feel that it will be worth a great deal to our world if we can keep in it such beautiful things as the cranes. One can only hope that the force of this belief will prove the stronger force.

GRAPH OF WHOOPING CRANE POPULATION

Aransas National Wildlife Refuge 1938–1965

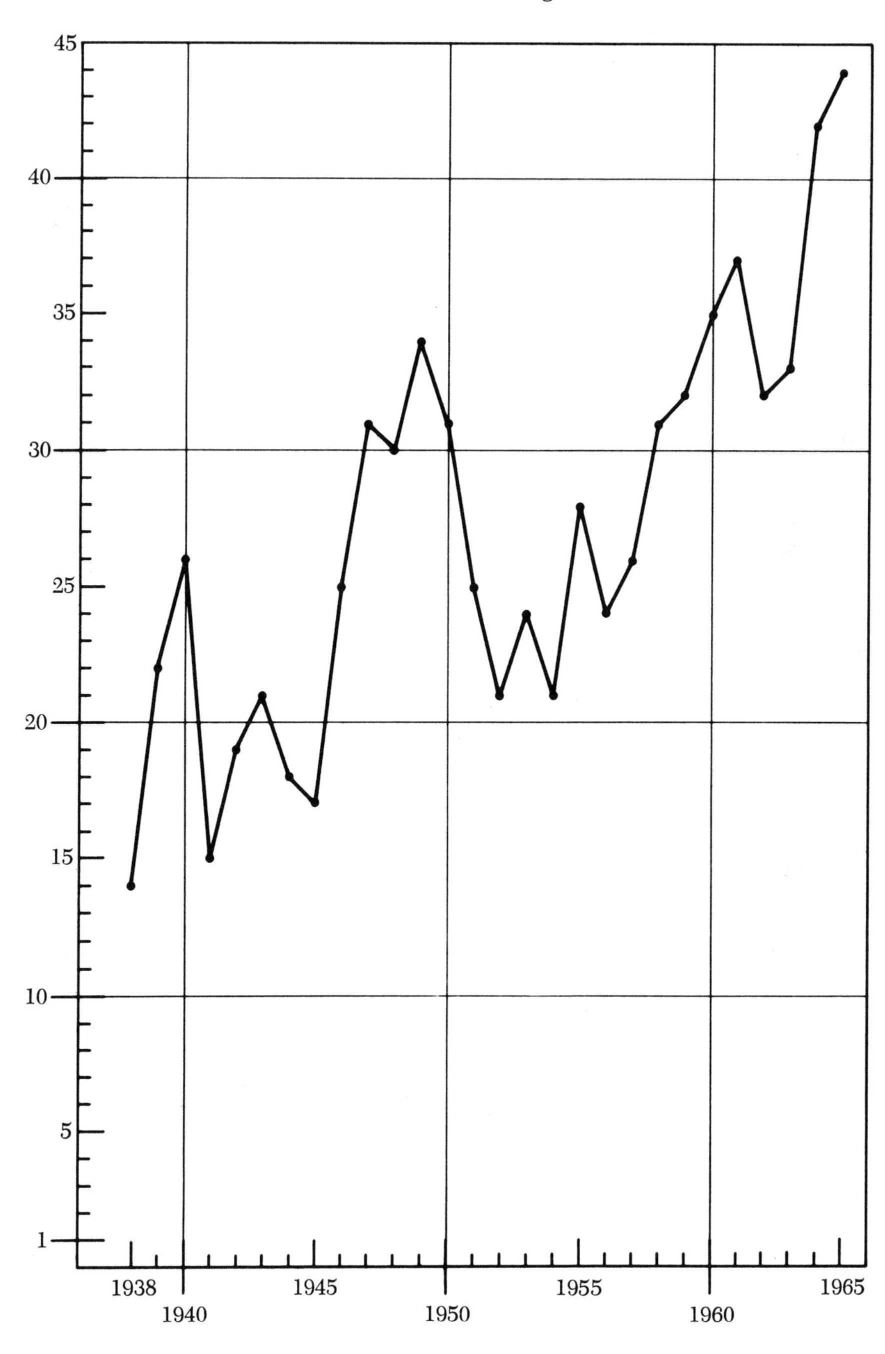

UNITED STATES
DEPARTMENT OF THE INTERIOR
Fish and Wildlife Service
Washington, D.C. 20240

WHOOPING CRANE SCOREBOARD

Whooping Cranes counted at Aransas National Wildlife Refuge since 1938

YEAR	YOUNG OF YEAR	ADULTS	TOTAL	ADULTS WITH YOUNG	NET LOSS	NET GAIN
38-39	4	10	14	8	Unknown	Unknown
39-40	6	16	22	8		8
40-41	5	21	26	8		4
41-42	2	13	15	4	11	
42-43	4	15	19	6		4
43-44	5	16	21	10		2
44-45	3	15	18	6	3	
45-46	3	14	17	4	1	
46-47	3	22	25	6		8
47-48	6	25	31	12		6
48-49	3	27	30	6	1	
49-50	4	30	34	8		4
50-51	5	26	31	8	3	
51-52	5	20	25	10	6	
52-53	2	19	21	4	4	
53-54	3	21	24	6		3
54-55	0	21	21	0	3	
55-56	8	20	28	12		7
56-57	2	22	24	4	4	
57-58	4	22	26	8		2
58-59	9	23	32	9 (4 pair and a single adult)		6
59-60	2	31	33	4		1
60-61	6	30	36	12		3
61-62	5	33	38	10		2
62-63	0	32	32	0	6	
63-64	7	26	33	No data	(One bird died at Aransas)	
64-65	10	32	42	9 (4 pair and a single adult)		9
65-66	8	36	44	16		2

Index